ILLINOIS CENTRAL COLLEGE
PN6101.P28
STACKS
The singing and the gold;

A12900 303155

PN
6101   PARKER   35193
.P28   The singing and the gold

WITHDRAWN

Illinois Central College
Learning Resource Center

GRANGERS

the singing
and the gold

by Elinor Parker

the singing
and the gold

Poems Translated from World Literature

Selected by Elinor Parker, 1906 - , comp.
Wood Engravings by Clare Leighton

THOMAS Y. CROWELL COMPANY · NEW YORK

ILLINOIS CENTRAL COLLEGE
LEARNING RESOURCE CENTER

35193

PN
6101
.P28

Copyright © 1962 by Elinor Parker
All rights reserved.
Designed by Albert Burkhardt
Manufactured in the United States of America
by the Vail-Ballou Press, Inc., Binghamton, New York
Library of Congress Catalog Card No. 62-16549
Fourth Printing

acknowledgments

For permission to reprint the copyrighted poems in this anthology, acknowledgment is
extended to the following:

THE AMERICAN-SCANDINAVIAN FOUNDATION for "Like an April Day" from *Anthology of Norwegian Lyrics*, translated by Charles Wharton Stork; "The Eternal" from *Anthology of
Swedish Lyrics*, translated by Charles Wharton Stork; "The Plants Stand Silent Around
Me" from *Book of Danish Verse*, translated by Robert Hillyer; "The Heather" and "The
Pearl" from *Second Book of Danish Verse*, translated by Charles Wharton Stork; "Rain"
from *Icelandic Poems and Stories*, translated by Watson Kirkconnell; "Song to Steingerd"
from *Pageant of Old Scandinavia*, translated by W. G. Collingwood and Jon Stefansson.
AUGUSTANA BOOK CONCERN for "Beauty is Most at Twilight's Close" from *Modern Swedish
Poems*, translated by G. Kenneth Laycock. By permission of Augustana Book Concern.
BEHRMAN HOUSE, INC. for "Tell Him" (Songs of the People 2) from *The Jewish Anthology*,
translated by Maurice Samuel. By permission. MRS. JETHRO BITHELL for "Evening Land-
scape" and "To the Sun" from *Contemporary Belgian Literature*, translated by Jethro
Bithell. PAUL BURLIN for Korosta Katzina Song ("Yellow Butterflies") from *The Indians'
Book*, translated by Natalie Curtis. CAMBRIDGE UNIVERSITY PRESS for "In the Spring" and
"A Window in the Breast" from the *Book of Greek Verse*, translated by Walter Headlam.
THE CLARENDON PRESS for permission for "The Climb to Virtue," "An Eclipse," and "Be
Still, My Soul" translated by C. M. Bowra, "How Can Man Die Better," "The Greek Dead
at Thermopylae," and "A Garden," translated by T. F. Higham, "The Beginning of Day"
by an anonymous translator, all from *The Oxford Book of Greek Verse in Translation;*
"Flute Song" from *Greek Poetry and Life*, translated by T. F. Higham; "Pangur Ban"
from *Translations from the Irish*, translated by Robin Flower. COLUMBIA UNIVERSITY PRESS
for "Autumn" from *Poems of Rainer Maria Rilke*, translated by Jessie Lemont. CONSTABLE
AND CO., LTD., for "The Morning Glory" from *Chinese Lyrics*, translated by Helen Waddell.
CRESSET PRESS LTD. for "Earth and Sea" by Pushkin, translated by Sir Cecil Kisch, from
The Waggon of Life. MRS. E. DARGUSH and LONGMANS, GREEN AND CO., LTD., for "Country
Music" from *The Spirit of Man*, translated by Robert Bridges. GEORGE DILLON for "Land-
scape" (1962 revision) from *Flowers of Evil*, translated by George Dillon. DOUBLEDAY AND
COMPANY, INC., for "Loneliness," "On the Mountain Pass," "At Matsushima," "The Rain-
Frogs," "Coolness," "The New and the Old," "Winter," "Parting," "Maple Leaves,"
"Summer Night," "The Sun Path," "On the Road to Nara," and "The Little Valley in
Spring," from *An Introduction to Haiku*, by Harold G. Henderson, copyright © 1958 by
Harold G. Henderson. By permission. "July" by Tatyanicheva translated by Babette

Deutsch from *Anthology of Russian Verse* by Avrahm Yarmolinsky, copyright © 1962 by Avrahm Yarmolinsky. Reprinted by permission of Doubleday & Company, Inc. DOUBLEDAY AND COMPANY, INC., and CONSTABLE AND CO., LTD., for "Take Him Earth for Cherishing" and "The Earth Is Sweet With Roses" from the Cathermerinon; "O Spring the Long-Desired" from Carmina Burana, and "In the Woods Alone," all from *The Wandering Scholars*, by Helen Waddell. E. P. DUTTON & CO., INC. for "Rondeau" from the book *Chanticleer: A Study of the French Muse*, translated by J. G. Legge. By permission. E. P. DUTTON & CO., INC. and J. M. DENT & SONS, LTD., for "The Miracle of Spring," "At Peace," "The Unseen Power," "As Salt Resolved in the Ocean" from *Persian Poems*, edited by A. J. Arberry. MAX EASTMAN for "Composed While Under Arrest" from *Poems of Five Decades*, translated by Max Eastman. Used with the permission of Max Eastman. THE FAITH PRESS, LTD., for "The Flute-Players" translated by Dorothy Blair, "Invocation" translated by G. H. Franz, "The Plover" translated by Dr. Alice Werner, and "Umamina" translated by R. M. Mfeka, all from *African Voices*, by Peggy Rutherfoord. MRS. HARRY FINE for "Peace" and "Love in Moonlight" from *Century of Indian Epigrams*, translated by Paul Elmer More. ANGEL FLORES for "Music" translated by Robert Fitzgerald and "The White Moon" translated by Kate Flores, from *An Anthology of French Poetry;* "An Arrow Flying Past" translated by J. M. Cohen, "The Moldering Hulk" translated by Kate Flores, "Immense Hour" translated by Edward F. Gahan, "I Know Not What I Seek Eternally" translated by Muriel Kittel, "Nightfall" translated by Eloise Roach, from *An Anthology of Spanish Poetry;* "Moon-Night" and "O Woodland Cool" translated by Mabel Cotterell, "Lovely as a Flower" and "Love Song" translated by Kate Flores, "The Wind's Song" translated by William R. Hughes, "Fain Would I Live in Safest Freedom" translated by Edwin Morgan, "The Pond," "Serenade" and "Nocturne" translated by Herman Salinger, "In Spring" translated by Vernon Watkins, from *An Anthology of German Poetry.* GROVE PRESS, INC., for "Bailada" by Airas Nunez, translated by Seth G. Thornton, from *Lyrics of the Middle Ages*, edited by Hubert Creekmore, copyright © 1959 by Grove Press, Inc., published by Grove Press, Inc. MRS. MOSES HADAS for "The Gusts of Winter Are Gone" from *The Greek Poets*, translated by Lewis P. Chamberlayne. HARCOURT, BRACE & WORLD, INC. for "Invitation to the Voyage" from *Things of This World*, © 1956 by Richard Wilbur. GEORGE C. HARRAP & CO., LTD., for "The Grave" and "Elegy for Lucy Lloyd" from *A Welsh Anthology*, translated by Ernest Rhys. DAVID HIGHAM ASSOCIATES, LTD., for "The Moon in the Mountains," "The Herd-Boy's Song," "On a Mountain Road," "The White Egret" and "Pear-Trees by the Fence" from *The Dragon Book*, translated by E. D. Edwards, published by William Hodge & Co., Ltd. MRS. ROBERT HILLYER for "The Dead Man Ariseth and Singeth a Hymn to the Sun" from *The Coming Forth by Day*, by Robert Hillyer, published by B. J. Brimmer & Co., 1923. THE HISPANIC SOCIETY OF AMERICA for "Song" by Gil Vicente, translated by Alice Jane McVan, from *Translations from Hispanic Poets.* Courtesy of The Society. THE HONORABLE SOCIETY OF CYMMRODORION for "A Snowy Day" from *Fifty Poems*, by Dafydd Ap Gwilym, translated by Idris H. Bell. HOUGHTON MIFFLIN COMPANY for "Neither Spirit Nor Bird" from *The American Rhythm*, by Mary Austin; "St. Teresa's Book Mark" and "Song" translated by H. W. Longfellow; "Love" and "Haroun's Favorite Song" translated by E. Powys Mathers. THE EXECUTORS OF DR. DOUGLAS HYDE for "My Grief on the Sea" translated by Douglas Hyde. THE JEWISH PUBLICATION SOCIETY OF AMERICA for "I Have Sought Thee Daily" from *Selected Religious Poems of Solomon Ibn Gabirol*, translated by Israel Zangwill. WATSON KIRKCONNELL for his translation of "To Sleep" by Jan Kochanowski, from *The Golden Treasury of Polish Lyrics.* ALFRED A. KNOPF, INC., for "Looking at the Moon" from *The Jade Mountain*, by Witter Bynner, copyright 1929 by Alfred A. Knopf, Inc. "The Hermit's Song" and "The Blackbird by Belfast Lough" from *Kings, Lords and Commons*, by Frank O'Connor, copyright 1959 by Frank O'Connor. ALFRED A. KNOPF, INC., and CONSTABLE AND CO., LTD., for "Reading the Book of Hills and Seas," "Sailing Homeward," "Pruning Trees," "I Built My Hut," "Song," "Crossing the River," "People Hide Their Love," and "Plucking the Rushes" from *170 Chinese Poems*, by Arthur Waley and Kuang Kang-Hu, copyright 1919, 1941 by Alfred A. Knopf, Inc.;

v

vi

renewal copyright 1947 by Arthur Waley. ALFRED A. KNOPF, INC., and GEORGE ALLEN AND UNWIN, LTD., for "Fighting South of the Ramparts" and "Planting Flowers on the Eastern Embankment" from *170 Chinese Poems* (Allen and Unwin) by Arthur Waley and Kuang Kang-Hu. Also for "Clearing at Dawn," "The Cranes," "The Pine-trees in the Courtyard," and "Dreaming That I Went with Li and Yu to Visit Yuan Chen," from *More Translations from the Chinese*, by Arthur Waley and Kuang Kang-Hu. Both copyright 1919, 1941 by Alfred A. Knopf, Inc.; renewal copyright 1947 by Arthur Waley. MRS. LUDWIG LEWISOHN for "The Youth Dreams" from *Modern German Poetry*, translated by Ludwig Lewisohn. F. L. LUCAS for "What a Piece of Work is Man," translated by F. L. Lucas, from *Poems 1935*. LUZAC & CO., LTD., for "Perfect Love" by Sana'I, from *Persian Poems*, translated by A. J. Arberry. THE MACMILLAN COMPANY and AVRAHM YARMOLINSKY for "Grapes" by Alexander Pushkin, "Black Diamond" by Nikolay Gumilyov, "With Wavering Feet I Walked" by Vladimir Soloyov, "A Magic Landscape" by Afanasy Fet, "Twilight," "Silentium" and "As Ocean Holds the Globe" by Fyodor Tyutchev, "In the Clear Cold" by Sergey Yesenin, "Remembrance" by Vasily Zhukovsky and "Upon the Hard Crest" by Anna Akhmatova, all from *A Treasury of Russian Verse*, by Avrahm Yarmolinsky, translated by Babette Deutsch, copyright © 1949 by The Macmillan Company. By permission of The Macmillan Company. THE MACMILLAN COMPANY, MACMILLAN & CO., LTD., THE MACMILLAN COMPANY OF CANADA, LTD., and THE TRUSTEES OF THE TAGORE ESTATE for "The Bird" (The Gardener LXVII) and "A Song Offering" (Gitanjali LVII) from *Collected Poems and Plays of Rabindranath Tagore*, copyright 1913, 1941. THE MENORAH JOURNAL for "An Old Song" by Yehoash, translated by Marie Syrkin. JOHN MURRAY for "Thy Garden" from the *Poems of Mu'tamid*, translated by Dulcie L. Smith. NATURAL HISTORY MAGAZINE for "A Lover's Lament" translated by H. J. Spinden, from "Home Songs of the Tewa Indians," *The American Museum Journal*, February, 1915. NEW DIRECTIONS for "The Infinite" by Giacomo Leopardi, from *The Signature of All Things*, by Kenneth Rexroth. THE EXECUTORS OF CURTIS HIDDEN PAGE for "Old Battlefield" (Seven Poems #5) from *Japanese Poetry*, translated by Curtis Hidden Page. ROBERT PAYNE for "A Rare Tree," "Conversation in the Mountains," "The Rain at Night," "Ninth Moon," from the *White Pony*. PHOENIX PRESS, London, for "Poem" by Hugo von Hofmannsthal, translated by Jethro Bithell and "Rima" by Gustavo Adolfo Becquer, translated by Harold Morland, from *Translation Series* (1945–47) Editors, Neville Braybooke and Elizabeth King. FREDERIC PROKOSCH for his translation of "When Love Has Passed Its Limits" from *Medea* by Euripides. RUTGERS UNIVERSITY PRESS for "Prayer," "The Sea," and "Thus Spoke My Love," translated by Adriaan J. Barnouw, from *Coming After*, edited by Adriaan J. Barnouw, copyright 1948 by The Trustees of Rutgers College in New Jersey. THE EXECUTORS OF WINIFRED M. RYDER for "True Friendship" from the *Panchatantra*, translated by Arthur W. Ryder. HERMAN SALINGER for "Love" by Johann Ludwig Tieck, translated by Herman Salinger. MARTIN SECKER & WARBURG, LTD., for "Mignon," translated by James Elroy Flecker. ESTELLA F. STUDIO for "Night" translated by Seumas O'Sullivan. TUPPER AND LOVE, INC., for "Where Shall We Dance" translated by Alice Stone Blackwell, from *1001 Poems of Mankind*, edited by Henry W. Wells. ARTHUR WALEY for "New Corn" and "Wild Geese" translated by Arthur Waley. ARTHUR WALEY and PERCY LUND HUMPHRIES & CO. LTD. for "Ono No Yoshiki" and "Nakatsukasa" from *Japanese Poetry*, *"The Uta,"* translated by Arthur Waley.

Foreword

It has been said many times that poetry when translated ceases to be poetry; there is even an Italian proverb, "to translate is to betray." The music must vanish and some of the magic goes with it. Imagine, for instance, Keats' "Ode to Autumn," or Shakespeare's "Fear No More the Heat of the Sun" in another language. Think, however, of the beauty of the Psalms in the King James Version of the Bible—what we should have lost if they had remained in their original Hebrew, unread by most of us, and what we have gained through the genius of the translators.

Many of us will probably learn a second language well enough to enjoy its literature in the original, a step beyond just understanding the words. Some will be able to add two, three, four, perhaps even five or six languages. A few may go further—a dozen, twenty—but I doubt whether anyone would become proficient in all the thirty-four languages from which these poems have been drawn. Through translation we can learn something of world literature; we can read poetry from all languages. The beauty of the thought remains, and, if the translator is also a poet, a new beauty of expression is found even though the original is lost.

Man's thoughts and emotions are basically the same the world over, no matter what tongue he speaks. He worships a Being greater than himself; he venerates his country or his tribe; he cares for his friends; he falls in love. He responds to nature, the alternating light and dark, the changing seasons. He refreshes his spirit with contemplation, with poetry and music, and he dreams. It is because of this universality that I have chosen to arrange the poems by subject rather than by the more conventional way of languages.

The title comes from a line in one of my favorite poems, Gilbert Murray's lovely translation from a Greek chorus which appears in the next to the last section of the book, for to me poetry is both music and treasure, singing and gold.

contents

how
sleep
the
brave

They fought south of the ramparts,
They died north of the wall.
They died in the moors and were not buried.
Their flesh was the food of crows.
"Tell the crows we are not afraid;
We have died in the moors and cannot be buried.
Crows, how can our bodies escape you?"
The waters flowed deep
And the rushes in the pool were dark.
The riders fought and were slain;
Their horses wander neighing.
By the bridge there was a house.
Was it south, was it north?
The harvest was never gathered.
How can we give you your offerings?
You served your Prince faithfully,
Though all in vain.
I think of you, faithful soldiers;
Your service shall not be forgotten.
For in the morning you went out to battle
And at night you did not return.

from the Chinese
Anonymous
Arthur Waley

4   Call to Youth

Let every Roman boy be taught to know
Constraining hardship as a friend, and grow
   Strong in fierce warfare, with dread lance and horse
Encountering the gallant Parthian foe.

Aye, let him live beneath the open sky
In danger. Him from leaguered walls should eye
   Mother and daughter of th' insurgent king,
And she for her betrothed, with many a sigh,

Should pray, poor maiden, lest, when hosts engage,
Unversed in arms he face that lion's rage
   So dangerous to trust what time he gluts
His wrath upon the battle's bloody stage.

For country 'tis a sweet and seemly thing
To die. Death ceases not from following
   E'en runaways. Can youth with feeble knees,
That fears to face the battle, 'scape his wing?

Defeat true manliness can never know:
Honors untarnished still it has to show.
   Not taking up or laying office down
Because the fickle mob will have it so.

'Tis Manliness lifts men too good to die,
And finds a way to that forbidden sky:
  Above the thronging multitudes, above
The clinging mists of earth it rises high.

Nor less abides to loyal secrecy
A sure reward: I would not have him be
  'Neath the same roof, the babbler who reveals
Demeter's secret things, or launch with me

A shallop frail: The god of heav'n has blent
Oft in one doom th' unclean and innocent:
  Seldom the miscreant has 'scaped the slow
And sure pursuit of halting punishment.

from the Latin
Horace
Hugh Vibart MacNaghten

Noble is he who falls in front of battle
　　bravely fighting for his native land;
and wretchedest the man who begs, a recreant,
　　citiless, from fertile acres fled.
Dear mother, ageing father, little children
　　drift beside him, and his wedded wife;
unwelcome he shall be, wherever turning,
　　press'd by want and hateful penury;
he shames his folk and cheats his glorious manhood;
　　all disgrace attends him, all despite.
Come then,—if beggars go unheard, uncared for,
　　spurn'd in life and in their children spurn'd—
with courage let us battle for our country,
　　freely spending life to save our sons.
Young men, stand firm and fight, stand one by other;
　　base retreat and rout let none begin.
Be high of heart, be strong in pride of combat;
　　grapple, self-forgetting, man to man.
Forbear to fly, deserting men grown older—
　　stiff about the knees, in honour old.
O foul reproach, when fallen with the foremost
　　lies an elder, hindermost the young—
a man whose head is white, whose beard is hoary,
　　breathing out his strong soul in the dust,
In nakedness his blood-wet members clutching—
　　foul reproach, a sight no gods condone!

Naked he lies where youth were better lying—
  sweet-flow'rd youth, that nothing misbecomes.
Grown men regard the young, women desire them—
  fair in life, in noble death still fair.
Be steadfast then, be strong and firmly rooted,
  grip the ground astride, press teeth to lip.

from the Greek
Tyrtaeus
T. F. Higham

Epitaph for Chaeroneia

These are the patriot brave, who side by side
Stood to their arms, and dash'd the foeman's pride:
Firm in their valour, prodigal of life,
Hades they chose the arbiter of strife;
That Greeks might ne'er to haughty victors bow,
Nor thraldom's yoke, nor dire oppression know;
They fought, they bled, and on their country's breast
(Such was the doom of heaven) these warriors rest.
Gods never lack success, nor strive in vain,
But man must suffer what the fates ordain.

from the Greek
Aristotle
C. R. Kennedy

The Greek Dead at Thermopylae

Great are the fallen of Thermopylae,
Nobly they ended, high their destination—
Beneath an altar laid, no more a tomb,
Where none with pity comes or lamentation,
But praise and memory—
A splendour of oblation
No rust shall blot nor wreckful Time consume.

The ground is holy: here the brave are resting,
And here Greek Honour keeps her chosen shrine.
Here too is one the worth of all attesting—
Leônidas, of Sparta's royal line,
Who left behind a gem-like heritage
Of courage and renown,
A name that shall go down
From age to age.

from the Greek
Simonides
T. F. Higham

Old battlefield, fresh with Spring flowers again—
  All that is left of the dream
Of twice ten thousand warriors slain.

from the Japanese
Matsuo Bashō
Curtis Hidden Page

Funeral Hymn

From the dead hand I take the bow he wielded,
To gain for us dominion, might, and glory.
Thou there, we hear, rich in heroic offspring,
Will vanquish all assaults of every foeman.

Approach the bosom of the earth, the mother,
This earth extending far and most propitious:
Young, soft as wool to bounteous givers, may she
Preserve thee from the lap of dissolution.

Open wide, O earth, press not heavily on him,
Be easy of approach, hail him with kindly aid;
As with a robe a mother hides
Her son, so shroud this man, O earth.

from the Sanskrit
Anonymous
Arthur A. Macdonell

Not to Die

These to their country brought an endless name,
When death's dark cloud around themselves they drew;
Nor dying, did they die: their virtue's fame
From Hades brings them back to live anew.

from the Greek
Simonides
John Hermann Merivale

friendship is a
sheltering tree

They told me, Heraclitus, they told me you were dead,
They brought me bitter news to hear and bitter tears to shed.
I wept as I remembered how often you and I
Had tired the sun with talking and sent him down the sky.

And now that thou art lying, my dear old Carian guest,
A handful of gray ashes, long, long ago at rest,
Still are thy pleasant voices, thy nightingales, awake;
For Death, he taketh all away, but them he cannot take.

> from the Greek
> *Callimachus*
> William Cory

Morning Star

Thou wert the morning star among the living,
   Ere thy fair light had fled;
Now, having died, thou art as Hesperus, giving
   New splendour to the dead.

> from the Greek
> *Plato*
> Percy Bysshe Shelley

Take him, earth, for cherishing,
To thy tender breast receive him.
Body of a man I give thee,
Noble even in its ruin. . . .

Once again the shining way
Leads to ample Paradise,
Leading to the woods again
That the Snake once lost for men.

Take, O take him, mighty Leader,
Bring again thy servant's soul
To that house from which he wandered.
Exiled, erring, long ago.

But for us, heap earth above him,
Earth with leaves and violets strewn,
Grave his name and pour the fragrant
Balm upon the icy stone.

from the Latin (Medieval)
Prudentius
Helen Waddell

Could we but see men as they are!
Could bare the breast, unpin it,
Hold it apart, and view the heart,
And read what lies within it;
Then close it fast again, and call
A friend a friend for all in all!

from the Greek
Anonymous
Walter Headlam

Remembrance

How many dear companions who enlivened for us
The world's rough road are gone, each fellow traveler
Much missed; yet say not sadly: they have left us!
But rather say, with gratitude: they were.

from the Russian
Vasily Zhukovsky
Babette Deutsch

When love has passed its limits
It brings no longer good:
It brings no peace or comfort to any soul.
Yet while she still moves mildly there is no fire
So sweet as that which is lit by the goddess of love.
Oh never, upon me, Cypris,
Send forth from your golden bow
The unerring arrow poisoned with desire!

Let my heart be temperate: for that
Is the wisest gift of the gods.
Let not that terrible goddess drive
Me to jealousy or rage! Oh let me never
Be one of those who incessantly are driven
To some new, forbidden longing!
Let her guide us gently toward the man we choose;
Let her bless our beds with repose.

O my country, my own home,
Let me never leave my city,
Let me never lose my way
In that dark and pitiless life
Where each new day brings sorrow!

O, let me first succumb
To death, yes, let me die
Before I suffer the hopeless
Grief of the loss of a home!

I have seen it with my own eyes,
I have heard my own heart tell me:
There is no city, no,
No friend who will give you pity
In the hour of your deepest woe.
O, let him perish in darkness
Who is faithless to his friends
And lets his heart stay frozen!
Let no such man be my friend!

from the Greek
Euripides
Frederic Prokosch

Slowly the flakes come down through the ash-gray skies and
  the shouting
Noises of life no more rise from the city below.

No loud shout from the cornland, nor rolling rumble of wagon,
No gay song of love, sung by the voices of youth.

Now from the market-tower through the air the hours are
  reported
Dimly as if by the stones, sighs from a world without sun.

Homeless birds on the tarnished windows are beating.—The
  souls of
Friends long dead return, watching me, calling to me.

Soon, dear friends, full soon—my passionate heart, be quiet—
Down to the silence I come, where I shall rest in the dark.

from the Italian
Giosuè Carducci
Asa Hughes

Dreaming That I Went with Li and Yü to Visit Yüan Chēn

(Written in Exile)

At night I dreamt I was back in Ch'ang-an;
I saw again the faces of old friends.
And in my dreams, under an April sky,
They led me by the hand to wander in the spring winds.
Together we came to the village of Peace and Quiet;
We stopped our horses at the gate of Yüan Chēn.
Yüan Chēn was sitting all alone;
When he saw me coming, a smile came to his face.
He pointed back at the flowers in the western court;
Then opened wine in the northern summer-house.
He seemed to be saying that neither of us had changed;
He seemed to be regretting that joy will not stay;
That our souls had met only for a little while,
To part again with hardly time for greeting.
I woke up and thought him still at my side;
I put out my hand; there was nothing there at all.

from the Chinese
Po Chü-i
Arthur Waley

'Tis hard to find in life
A friend, a bow, a wife,
Strong, supple to endure,
In stock and sinew pure,
In time of danger sure.

False friends are common. Yes, but where
True nature links a friendly pair,
The blessing is as rich as rare.

To bitter ends
You trust true friends,
Not wife nor mother,
Not son nor brother.

No long experience alloys
True friendship's sweet and supple joys;
No evil men can steal the treasure;
'Tis death, death only, sets a measure.

from the Sanskrit
The Panchatantra
Arthur W. Ryder

arise my love, my fair one

Upon the Hard Crest

Upon the hard crest of a snowdrift
We tread, and grown quiet, we walk
On towards my house, white, enchanted;
Our mood is too tender for talk.

And sweeter than song is this dream now
Come true, the low boughs of the firs
That sway as we brush them in passing,
The slight silver clink of your spurs.

from the Russian
Anna Akhmatova
Babette Deutsch

Tolling Bells

The bells are tolling,
Bidding all to rest.
But you being for ever on my mind,
I cannot sleep.

from the Japanese
Lady Kasa
Ishii and Obata

Black Diamond

Black velvet where a shining diamond
Forgotten lies,
To that I can compare the look that nigh
Sings in her eyes.

Her porcelain body's whiteness is too vague,
Too sweet a boon,
Like a white lilac blossom dim beneath
A dying moon.

Within her soft and waxen hands the blood
Burns hot and bright
As an eternal candle set within
The Virgin's sight.

And all of her is airy as a bird
That would fly forth
On a clear day in autumn, taking leave
Of the sad North.

from the Russian
Nikolay Gumilyov
Babette Deutsch

My love, my love, thus spoke my love to me,
While on her delicate lips my lips were browsing.
Those words, too clear to be in need of glozing,
Entered my ears and stirred mysteriously
My inmost thoughts into tumultuous stress.
They did not trust the ear and, at their pressure,
I begged my dearest for a fuller measure
Of that confession, and she did confess.
Oh bounty of the heart that overflows!
Entranced, each heart did other's heart imprison.
But when the morning star fled for the risen
Light of the sun, the sad truth too arose:
Oh Gods, how close are things that are and seem.
How like the dream is life, like life the dream.

from the Dutch
Pieter Corneliszoon Hooft
A. J. Barnouw

The voice of my beloved! behold, he cometh
Leaping upon the mountains, skipping upon the hills.
My beloved is like a roe or a young hart:
Behold, he standeth behind our wall,
He looketh forth at the windows,
Shewing himself through the lattice.
My beloved spake, and said unto me,
"Rise up, my love, my fair one, and come away.
For, lo, the winter is past,
The rain is over and gone;
The flowers appear on the earth;
The time of the singing of birds is come,
And the voice of the turtle is heard in our land;
The fig tree putteth forth her green figs,
And the vines with the tender grape
Give a good smell.
Arise, my love, my fair one, and come away.
O my dove, that art in the clefts of the rock, in the secret places
    of the stairs,
Let me see thy countenance, let me hear thy voice;
For sweet is thy voice, and thy countenance is comely."

                ·   ·   ·

My beloved is mine, and I am his:
He feedeth among the lilies.
Until the day breaks, and the shadows flee away,

Turn, my beloved, and be thou like a roe or a young hart
Upon the mountains of Bether.

.   .   .

Awake, O north wind; and come,
                thou south;
Blow upon my garden, that the
        spices thereof may flow out.
Let my beloved come into his garden,
And eat his pleasant fruits.

from the Hebrew
The Old Testament
King James Version

In the Woods Alone

I have been in the woods alone,
        I have loved hidden places.
Tumult of men I shun
        And the crowding faces.
Now the snow vanishes,
        Out the leaves start,
The nightingale's singing:
Love's in the heart.

from the Latin (Medieval)
Anonymous
Helen Waddell

Who would be loved, let him possess
   A true beloved like mine,
And share in secret blessedness
   Love's mystery divine:
Lovers like us none else, I guess,
   Are found in earth's confine.

'Soul of the world'—such was the name
   My idol gàve to me;
While I do live, her I proclaim
   Soul of my world to be,
And none I know doth own the same
   Dear loyalty as she.

Behold me now—take not as heard,
   But ask, and all will say
That this is sooth: this was her word:
   'I shall be thine for aye.'
Truly she is, as she averred,
   And I am hers alway.

from the Persian
Sana'i
A. J. Arberry

> Love must think in music sweetly,
> for all thought is too remote.
> Only music can denote
> all that love desires completely.
> Love we know and know her only
> when the voice of music sounds;
> while her magic still abounds,
> love can never leave us lonely.
> Love would die a sterile death,
> did not music lend her breath.

from the German
Ludwig Tieck
Herman Salinger

Thy Garden

My thoughts are as a garden-plot, that knows
No rain but of thy giving, and no rose
Except thy name. I dedicate it thine,
My garden, full of fruits in harvest time.

from the Arabian
Mu'tamid, King of Seville
Dulcie L. Smith

January Night

January night, quiet and luminous,
near the river, among the rocks, at your side,

My heart ripe
for marvel and miracle,

If a star fell,
I should hold out my hand . . .

from the Spanish
Rafael Alberto Arrieta
Muna Lee de Muñoz Marin

Like an April Day

The buds of April dare not yet unfold
Their eager store of beauty to the sight,
While spring still battles with the winter's cold.

The broken sunbeams are but faintly bright,
The blossom swells within its narrow bower
In longing silence as it drinks the light.

Already it divines the Maytime hour
At whose brave touch the clouds will melt away
And cold no more constrain the heart-shaped flower.

Lover, your sweetheart's like an April day:
These chilly looks, the arrows of her glance—
You cannot tell as yet what they would say.

Her little heart, too, may be all adance,
As the unrest in it wells ever higher,
Her lips would gladly smile, had they the chance.

Soon May will kiss the longing leaves with fire,
Soon through the air the wingèd loves will dart,
And if you then dare show your deep desire,
The flower will then reveal its blossom-heart.

from the Norwegian
Johan Sebastian C. Wellhaven
Charles Wharton Stork

Off with sleep, love, up from bed,
  This fair morn;
See, for our eyes the rosy red
  New dawn is born;
Now that skies are glad and gay
In this gracious month of May,
  Love me, sweet;
Fill my joy in brimming measure;
In this world he hath no pleasure
  That will none of it.

Come, love, through the woods of spring,
  Come walk with me;
Listen, the sweet birds jargoning
  From tree to tree.
List and listen, over all
Nightingale most musical
  That ceases never;
Grief begone, and let us be
For a space as glad as he;
  Time's flitting ever.

Old Time, that loves not lovers, wears
  Wings swift in flight;
All our happy life he bears
  Far in the night.

Old and wrinkled on a day,
Sad and weary shall you say,
 "Ah, fool was I,
That took no pleasure in the grace
Of the flower that from my face
 Time has seen die."

Leave then sorrow, teen, and tears
 Till we be old;
Young we are, and of our years
 Till youth be cold.
Pluck the flower; while Spring is gay
In this happy month of May
 Love me, love;
Fill our joy in brimming measure;
In this world he hath no pleasure
 That will none thereof.

from the French
Jean Passerat
Andrew Lang

Who was it, tell me, that first of men reckon'd
Time by the hour and the minute and second?
A soulless man, without heart or light,
He sat and he mused in the long winter's night,
And counted the pittering steps of the mouse,
And the pick of the woodworm that gnawed at the house.

Kisses, now tell me, who first did discover?
It was the warm happy mouth of a lover;
He kiss'd without ceasing, he kiss'd without care,
He kiss'd his first kiss in the May-season fair;
The flowers from their emerald cradle upsprang,
The sun brightly beam'd, the birds sweetly sang.

from the German
Heinrich Heine
Richard Garnett

I'll twine white violets and the myrtle green;
Narcissus will I twine and lilies sheen;
I'll twine sweet crocus and the hyacinth blue;
And last I twine the rose, love's token true:
That all may form a wreath of beauty, meet
To deck my Heliodora's tresses sweet.

from the Greek
Meleager
Goldwin Smith

Ono No Yoshiki

My love
Is like the grasses
Hidden in the deep mountain:
Though its abundance increases,
There is none that knows.

from the Japanese
Kokin Shū
Arthur Waley

The invisible atoms of the air
Quiver all about, and flare;
The sky is splintered into golden light;
The earth trembles with delight;
I hear as they float on waves of song
The whisper of a kiss, the beat of a wing;
My lids are closed . . . What can it be?
O love is passing by!

from the Spanish
Gustavo Adolfo Bécquer
Harold Morland

Neither Spirit nor Bird

Neither spirit nor bird;
That was my flute you heard
Last night by the river.
When you came with your wicker jar
Where the river drags the willows,
That was my flute you heard,
Wacoba, Wacoba,
Calling, Come to the willows!

Neither the wind nor a bird
Rustled the lupine blooms.
That was my blood you heard
Answer your garment's hem
Whispering through the grasses;
That was my blood you heard
By the wild rose under the willows.
That was no beast that stirred,
That was my heart you heard,
Pacing to and fro
In the ambush of my desire,
To the music my flute let fall.
Wacoba, Wacoba,
That was my heart you heard
Leaping under the willows.

from the Shoshone (American Indian)
Anonymous
Mary Austin

Come Mamina,
Come let us stretch our legs and thither **go,**
There where it is wilderness,
There where water fountains spring
Dampening the deep green rocks,
Slippery with slimy moss.

Nay Mamina,
Come out as though to draw water,
Carry a calabash and descend to the river.
There you will find me under the water-myrtle
Heavy in full bloom,
Black and oozing with thick juice.

Come Mamina,
Alone, you are bright with crimson hue,
Your path adorned with gaudy colours,
Blossoming with flowers,
Which stoop before you
Bowing their heads on the earth.

Come Mamina,
When you did gaze on me, ebony maiden,
I knew not whither I would go,
My knees quivered, my weapons dropped,

I was filled with the bitterness that lurks in the heart
Like a wild beast, and is called love.

Alas, I seek you, Mamina,
You have hidden in the fields of dry grass.
The dry grass is my soul,
Yet you are loitering there,
Gathering blackberries, herbs and creepers.

It is not the national song of shields and knobkerries I sing.
In truth I chant in harmony with the music of your reed-pipe,
Whose tunes I hear in the land of Chaka.
I heard and listened and knew.
I beheld your dark-complexioned lips
Close over the singing reed-pipe,
Which recalls the golden-rumped canary of the forest.
I would that it were blown by the heart
Which harbours thought and feeling.
You have made me grow thus with love,
That I no more appear as a Zulu
Within the courtyard of the black people.

Your love and mine, O Mamina,
Excel the mind, beyond the power of the diviners,
Whose magic bones are strewn on the ground.
They grind herbs and poisonous bushes.
'In truth, are you not deceiving me, Mamina?'
I ask you, as I gaze into

The center of your eyes without blinking:
'Are you not one of the ancestral spirits?'
Perchance you have lost your way,
On your journey to the gates of Heaven,
And have branched off to Earth
And chanced on the roots of love.

Come Mamina,
You are the star of my soul,
You alone are in the depth of my veins
Which make my heart tremble.
You are like the track of the field rat
Which winds through old grass and heads far off.

Come Mamina,
I feel loneliness steal over me.
This earth affords no refuge for me.
Come and lead me to your land, Mamina.
There let us solve the mystery of this love,
That I may know it, Mamina;
Know it wholly with the spirit of the ancestors.

from the Zulu (African)
B. W. Vilikazi
R. M. Mfeka

Grace and beauty has the maid;
Could anything more lovely be?

Sailor, you who live on ships,
Did you ever see
Any ship or sail or star
As beautiful as she?

Knight of war, in armour clad,
Did you ever see
Horse or arms or battlefield
As beautiful as she?

Shepherd, you who guard your flock,
Did you ever see
Cattle, vale, or mountain range
As beautiful as she?

from the Portuguese
Gil Vicente
Alice Jane McVan

Green rushes with red shoots,
Long leaves bending to the wind—
You and I in the same boat
Plucking rushes at the Five Lakes.
We started at dawn from the orchid-island:
We rested under the elms till noon.
You and I plucking rushes
Had not plucked a handful when night came!

from the Chinese
Anonymous
Arthur Waley

Once Only

Once—only once,
I saw him in the light
Of the sky-wandering moon;
Now I see him in my dreams.

from the Japanese
Ato Tobira
Ishii and Obata

Light, my light, the world-filling light, the eye-kissing light, heart-sweetening light!

Ah, the light dances, my darling, at the center of my life; the light strikes, my darling, the chords of my love; the sky opens, the wind runs wild, laughter passes over the earth.

The butterflies spread their sails on the sea of light. Lilies and jasmines surge up on the crest of the waves of light.

The light is shattered into gold on every cloud, my darling, and it scatters gems in profusion.

Mirth spreads from leaf to leaf, my darling, and gladness without measure. The heaven's river has drowned its banks and the flood of joy is abroad.

from the Sanskrit
Rabindranath Tagore
Rabindranath Tagore

I could not keep love down:
He rose and pinned my sleepy eyes awake,
He crept into my voice and made it break,
  My heart, and made it ache.

I could not keep love down:
He rose and lighted fires within my brain,
And all the waters of the world are vain
  To put them out again.

from the Arabian
The Thousand Nights and One Night
E. Powys Mathers

O Woodland Cool

O woodland cool,
Where rustlest thou
Wherein my love doth stray?
O echo, tell
Where listenest thou
Who understands my lay?

O echoing sound,
O singst thou her
The dreams I like the most,
The ballads all
O bring them her
Whom I so early lost!

Deep in my heart
The rustling wood
Wherein my love doth stray;
In sorrows slept
The echoing sound,
The tunes have blown away.

In woodland am
I so alone,
O dearest, come to me;
Though many a song
Away has flown,
Others I'll sing to thee!

from the German
Clemens Brentano
Mabel Cotterell

Who says that it's by my desire,
This separation, this living so far from you?
My dress still smells of the perfume that you wore;
My hand still holds the letter that you sent.
Round my waist I wear a double sash;
I dream that it binds us both with a same-heart knot,
Did you know that people hide their love,
Like a flower that seems too precious to be picked?

from the Chinese
Wu-Ti, Emperor of Liang
Arthur Waley

Women's Eyes

The world is full of women's eyes,
Defiant, filled with sly surprise,
Demure, a little overfree,
Or simply sparkling roguishly;
It seems a gorgeous lily-bed,
Whichever way I turn my head.

from the Sanskrit
Bhartrihari
Arthur W. Ryder

Crossing the river I pluck hibiscus-flowers:
In the orchid-swamps are many fragrant herbs.
I gather them, but who shall I send them to?
My love is living in lands far away.
I turn and look towards my own country:
The long road stretches on for ever.
The same heart, yet a different dwelling:
Always fretting, till we are grown old!

from the Chinese
Anonymous
Arthur Waley

Love

Love was before the light began,
When light is over, love shall be;
O warm hand in the grave, O bridge of truth,
O ivy's tooth
Eating the green heart of the tree
Of man!

from the Arabian
The Thousand Nights and One Night
E. Powys Mathers

The sea hath its pearls,
　The heaven hath its stars;
But my heart, my heart,
　My heart hath its love.

Great are the sea and the heaven;
　Yet greater is my heart,
And fairer than pearls or stars
　Flashes and beams my love.

Thou little, youthful maiden,
　Come into my great heart;
My heart, and the sea and the heaven
　Are melting away with love!

from the German
Heinrich Heine
Henry Wadsworth Longfellow

There is a myth, a tale men tell:
Each mussel shell
That in the ocean's bitter deep doth lie,
When it has wrought its pearl, must straightway die.
O Love, thou art the pearl my heart hath made,
And I am sore afraid.

from the Danish
Hans Christian Andersen
Charles Wharton Stork

Song to Steingerd

There breaks on me, burning upon me,
A blaze from the cheeks of a maiden,
—I laugh not to look on the vision—
In the light of the hall by the doorway.
So sweet and so slender I deem her,
Though I spy but a glimpse of an ankle
By the threshold:—and through me there flashes
A thrill that shall age never more.

from the Old Norse
Cormac Ogmundarson
W. G. Collingwood and Jon Stefansson

50 *A Young Bride*

Like the sweet apple which reddens upon the topmost bough,
A-top on the topmost twig,—which the pluckers forgot some-
how,—
Forgot it not, nay, but got it not, for none could get it till now.

Like the wild hyacinth flower, which on the hills is found,
Which the passing feet of the shepherds for ever tear and
wound,
Until the purple blossom is trodden into the ground.

from the Greek
Sappho
D. G. Rossetti

The Morning Glory

The morning glory climbs above my head,
Pale flowers of white and purple, blue and red.
I am disquieted.

Down in the withered grasses something stirred;
I thought it was his footfall that I heard.
　　Then a grasshopper chirred.

I climbed the hill just as the new moon showed,
I saw him coming on the southern road.
　　My heart lays down its load.

from the Chinese
Confucius
Helen Waddell

Arrows of Love

　　Where are you going, winsome maid,
　　Through deepest, darkest night? (he said.)
　　I go to him whom love has made
　　Dearer to me than life (she said.)
　　Ah, girl, and are you not afraid,
　　For you are all alone? (he said.)
　　The god of love shall be mine aid,
　　Arrows of love fly true (she said.)

from the Sanskrit
Chauras
E. Powys Mathers

On a hill there blooms a palm
'Twixt Tigris and Euphrates old,
And among the leafy branches
Sits the phoenix, bird of gold.

Bird of gold, go forth and find me
Him whose bride I am to be:
Search and circle till thou find him,
Bind him, bring him, bird, to me.

If thou hast no thread of scarlet,
Give him greeting without end:
Tell him, golden bird, my spirit
Languishes towards my friend.

Tell him: Now the garden blossoms,
Closed except to his command;
Mid the leaves the golden apple
Waits and trembles for his hand.

Tell him, nightly on my pillow
Wakes the longing without name,
And the whiteness of my body
Burns my couch as with a flame.

If he comes not, hear my secret:
All prepared my coffer stands;
Linen, silk, and twenty singlets
Wrought and knitted by these hands.

And the softest of all feathers
By my mother plucked and stored:
Through the nights she filled the cushions
For her daughter's bridal hoard.

And the bridal veil of silver
Waits to deck me when I marry:
Bride and dowry, both are ready—
Wherefore does the bridegroom tarry?

.   .   .

Seethe and whisper, magic potion:
Thus the phoenix makes reply:
"In the night to thy beloved
With my secret will I fly.

"In his dreams I give thy greeting,
In his dreams reveal thy face:
Lo! Upon a broomstick mounted
Unto thee he flies apace.

54 "And he comes and speaks; 'Behold me,
Oh, my joy, my hope, my pride:
Not with golden gifts or dowry,
But with love become my bride.

" 'Gold and silk I have aplenty—
Fire of youth and ringlets fine:
Both I give thee—swiftly, lightly,
Come to me, beloved mine.' "

. . .

When the night was dark above me
And the stars with clouds were stilled,
On his quest the phoenix vanished—
And his words are unfulfilled.

And at morn, at noon, at even,
Still I watch the clouds of fire:
"Clouds above me, answer, Wherefore
Comes he not, my heart's desire?"

from the Hebrew
Chaim Nachman Bialik
Maurice Samuel

When stubble-lands were greening, you came among the
    stooks,
And grace was in your feet then, and love was in your looks,
In your cheeks the rose grew redder, and your hair in clusters
    lay,
And I would we lived together, or together slipped away.

I had a dream on Wednesday that bitter was the frost,
And I saw my love lamenting at dawn that I was lost;
Methought I came beside her and held her tenderly,
And all Erin I defied then to part my love and me.

My curse on him is spoken who keeps my love from me,
And swears that to our courting he never will agree;
For though skies should send the deluge or the snowy North
    its flakes,
We two could live as pleasant as the swans upon the lakes.

The sea-gull's heart is merry when the fish is in his beak,
And the eel within Lough Eyrne can swim from creek to creek,
And I spoke tripping Gaelic, and merry songs I've sung,
But now my wits are crazy and leaden is my tongue.

from the Irish
Anonymous
Patrick Browne

My child, my sister, dream
How sweet all things would seem
Were we in that kind land to live together
  And there love slow and long,
  There love and die among
Those scenes that image you, that sumptuous weather.
  Drowned suns that glimmer there
  Through cloud-disheveled air
Move me with such a mystery as appears
  Within those other skies
  Of your treacherous eyes
When I behold them shining through their tears.

There, there is nothing else but grace and measure,
Richness, quietness, and pleasure.

  Furniture that wears
  The luster of the years
Softly would glow within our glowing chamber,
  Flowers of rarest bloom
  Proffering their perfume
Mixed with the vague fragrances of amber;
  Gold ceilings would there be,
  Mirrors deep as the sea,
The walls all in an Eastern splendor hung—

Nothing but should address
The soul's loneliness,
Speaking her sweet and native tongue.

There, there is nothing else but grace and measure,
Richness, quietness, and pleasure.

See, sheltered from the swells
There in the still canals
Those drowsy ships that dream of sailing forth;
It is to satisfy
Your least desire, they ply
Hither through all the waters of the earth.
The sun at close of day
Clothes the fields of hay,
Then the canals, at last the town entire
In hyacinth and gold:
Slowly the land is rolled
Sleepward under a sea of gentle fire.

There, there is nothing else but grace and measure,
Richness, quietness, and pleasure.

from the French
Charles Baudelaire
Richard Wilbur

Put your head, darling, darling, darling,
Your darling black head my heart above;
Oh, mouth of honey, with the thyme for fragrance,
Who, with heart in breast, could deny you love?

Oh, many and many a young girl for me is pining,
Letting her locks of gold to the cold wind free,
For me, the foremost of our gay young fellows;
But I'd leave a hundred, pure love, for thee!

Then put your head, darling, darling, darling,
Your darling black head my heart above;
Oh, mouth of honey, with the thyme for fragrance,
Who, with heart in breast, could deny you love?

from the Irish
Anonymous
Samuel Ferguson

My little breath, under the willows by the water-side we used
    to sit,
And there the yellow cottonwood bird came and sang.
That I remember and therefore I weep.
Under the growing corn we used to sit,
And there the little leaf bird came and sang.
That I remember and therefore I weep.
There on the meadow of yellow flowers we used to walk.
Alas! how long ago that we two walked in that pleasant way.
Then everything was happy, but alas! how long ago.
There on the meadow of crimson flowers we used to walk.
Oh, my little breath, now I go there alone in sorrow.

from the Tewa (American Indian)
Anonymous
H. J. Spinden

Love Song

How am I to withhold my soul
That it not impinge on yours? How am I
To bear it beyond you toward any other?
Ah, gladly would I set it apart
As in darkness lost in some strange
Still place where it would not vibrate
Whenever in your depths it vibrates.
But everything we are touched by, you and I,
Draws us together as the stroke of a bow
Mingles two strings in a single note.
Upon what instrument have we been strung?
And in the hands of what musician are we held?
Oh, sweet song.

from the German
Rainer Maria Rilke
Kate Flores

My lady carries love within her eyes;
  All that she looks on is made pleasanter;
  Upon her path men turn to gaze at her;
He whom she greeteth feels his heart to rise,
And droops his troubled visage, full of sighs,
  And of his evil heart is then aware:
  Hate loves, and pride becomes a worshipper.
O women, help to praise her in somewise.
Humbleness, and the hope that hopeth well,
  By speech of hers into the mind are brought,
  And who beholds is blessed oftenwhiles.
  The look she hath when she a little smiles
  Cannot be said, nor holden in the thought;
'Tis such a new and gracious miracle.

from the Italian
Dante Alighieri
D. G. Rossetti

My grief on the sea,
How the waves of it roll!
For they heave between me
And the love of my soul!

Abandoned, forsaken,
To grief and to care,
Will the sea ever waken
Relief from despair?

My grief, and my trouble!
Would he and I were
In the province of Leinster,
Or county of Clare.

Were I and my darling—
Oh, heart-bitter wound!—
On board of the ship
For America bound.

On a green bed of rushes
All last night I lay,
And I flung it abroad
With the heat of the day.

And my love came behind me—
He came from the south;
His breast to my bosom,
His mouth to my mouth.

from the Irish
Anonymous
Douglas Hyde

Night

The Moon is gone
And the Pleiads set,
Midnight is nigh;
Time passes on,
And passes, yet
Alone I lie.

from the Greek
Sappho
J. M. Edmonds

An early dew woos the half-opened flowers,
  Wind of the south, dear child,
Close clings about their stalks for drunken hours;
  And yet your eyes, dear child,
  Cool pools which rise, dear child,
    High in the mountains of my soul,
    These, these
  The lips have drunken whole;
  And yet your mouth, dear child,
    Your mouth, dear child, is envied of the bees.

from the Arabian
The Thousand Nights and One Night
E. Powys Mathers

Love in Moonlight

My love within a forest walked alone,
All in a moonlit dale;
And here awhile she rested, weary grown,
And from her shoulders threw the wimpled veil
To court the little gale.

I peering through the thicket saw it all,
The yellow moonbeams fall,
I saw them mirrored from her bosom fly
Back to the moon on high.

from the Sanskrit
Bhartrihari
Paul Elmer More

I Love Long Black Eyes

Even now
I love long black eyes that caress like silk,
Ever and ever sad and laughing eyes,
Whose lids make such sweet shadow when they close
It seems another beautiful look of hers,
I love a fresh mouth, ah, a scented mouth,
And curving hair, subtle as a smoke,
And light fingers, and laughter of green gems.

from the Sanskrit
Chauras
E. Powys Mathers

Let's dance now, all of us, all of us, oh my maidens,
under these little trees of flowering hazel,
and any girl who is fair as us fair ladies,
if loving a friend perchance,
under these little trees of flowering hazel,
will come to the dance!

Let's dance now, all of us, all of us, oh companions,
under the hazel thicket's spreading branches,
and any girl who's handsome as we are handsome,
if loving a friend perchance,
under the hazel thicket's spreading branches,
will come to the dance!

By God, oh maidens, while we have the time to do it,
under these flowered sprays, let's dance in beauty,
and she who looks as fair as we are looking,
if loving a friend perchance,
under these branches where we dance in blossoms,
will come to the dance!

from the Portuguese (Galician)
Airas Nunez
Seth G. Thornton

35193

Now the bright crocus flames, and now
   The slim narcissus takes the rain,
And, straying o'er the mountain's brow,
   The daffodillies bud again.
The thousand blossoms wax and wane
   On wold, and heath, and fragrant bough,
   But fairer than the flowers art thou
Than any growth of hill or plain.

Ye gardens cast your leafy crown,
That my love's feet may tread it down,
   Like lilies on the lilies set;
My Love, whose lips are softer far
Than drowsy poppy petals are,
   And sweeter than the violet!

from the Greek
Meleager
Andrew Lang

Winter, now thy spite is spent,
Frost and ice and branches bent!
Fogs and furious storms are o'er,
Sloth and torpor, sorrow frore,
Pallid wrath, lean discontent.

Comes the graceful band of May!
Cloudless shines the limpid day,
Shine by night the Pleiades;
While a grateful summer breeze
Makes the season soft and gay.

Golden Love! shine forth to view!
Souls of stubborn men subdue!
See me bend! What is thy mind?
Make the girl thou givest kind,
And a leaping ram's thy due!

O the jocund face of earth,
Breathing with young grassy birth!
Every tree with foliage clad,
Singing birds in greenwood glad,
Flowering fields for lovers' mirth!

from the Latin (Medieval)
Anonymous
J. A. Symonds

In the courtyard grows a rare tree
With green leaves and a splendid flowering.
Lifting myself to the branch, I cut down some blossoms;
I shall send them to him on whom my heart dwells.
The sweet smell fills my sleeves and lap.
The distance is too great for it ever to reach you.
Moreover, such a gift would hardly please you.
Now I know how long you have been away.

from the Chinese
Nineteen Han Poems
Anonymous

Softly sighs the April air,
    Ere the coming of the May;
Of the tranquil night aware,
    Murmur nightingale and jay;
Then, when dewy dawn doth rise,
    Every bird in his own tongue
Wakes his mate with happy cries;
    All their joy abroad is flung.

Gladness, lo! is everywhere
    When the first leaf sees the day;
And shall I alone despair,
    Turning from sweet love away?
Something to my heart replies,
    Thou too wast for rapture strung;
Wherefore else the dreams that rise
    Round thee when the year is young?

One, than Helen yet more fair,
    Loveliest blossom of the May,
Rose-tints hath and sunny hair,
    And a gracious mien and gay;

Heart that scorneth all disguise,
   Lips where pearls of truth are hung,—
God, who gives all sovereignties,
   Knows her like was never sung.

Though she lead through long despair,
   I would never say her nay,
If one kiss—reward how rare!—
   Each new trial might repay.
Swift returns I'd then devise,
   Many labors, but not long.
Following so fair a prize
   I could nevermore go wrong.

from the Provençal
Arnaut Daniel
Harriet Waters Preston

Yea, let me praise my lady whom I love:
  Likening her unto the lily and rose:
  Brighter than morning star her visage glows;
She is beneath even as her Saint above;
She is as the air in summer which God wove
  Of purple and of vermilion glorious;
  As gold and jewels richer than man knows.
Love's self, being love for her, must holier prove.
Ever as she walks she hath a sober grace,
  Making bold men abashed and good men glad;
  If she delight thee not, thy heart must err.
No man dare look on her, his thoughts being base:
  Nay, let me say even more than I have said;—
  No man could think base thoughts who looked on her.

from the Italian
Guido Guinicelli
D. G. Rossetti

Beauty in woman; the high will's decree;
  Fair knighthood armed for manly exercise;
  The pleasant song of birds; love's soft replies;
The strength of rapid ships upon the sea;
The serene air when light begins to be;
  The white snow, without wind that falls and lies;
  Fields of all flower; the place where waters rise;
Silver and gold; azure in jewelry:
Weighed against these the sweet and quiet worth
  Which my dear lady cherishes at heart
    Might seem a little matter to be shown;
  Being truly, over these, as much apart
As the whole heaven is greater than this earth.
  All good to kindred natures cleaveth soon.

from the Italian
Guido Cavalcanti
D. G. Rossetti

Here's a summer, heavy and hard;
Here's a black world for the bard!
Ah, song, what summer should this be,
To break the heart of melody!
Now to the north, this mourning day,
Sun nor moon send any ray;
Since she, the moon of womankind,
Lies in the clay now, cold and blind:
And, nailed in by the oaken lid,
Her comely lovely form is hid.

Ah, silver candle of the north,
How wert thou carried, earth to earth?
My soul, arise, and where I wait
Open to me the earthen gate,—
Forget thy grave and gravelled place,
And let me see thee face to face;
For truly by thy grave stands one
Who has no pleasure in the sun,—
Sad lingerer, that gave to thee
His heart, his hope, his melody.

from the Welsh
Llewelyn Goch
Ernest Rhys

O Golden Love, what life, what joy but thine?
  Come death when thou art gone and make an end!
When gifts and tokens are no longer mine,
  Nor the sweet intimacies of a friend.
These are the flowers of youth. But painful age,
  The bane of beauty, following swiftly on,
Wearies the heart of man with sad presage
  And takes away his pleasure in the sun.
Hateful is he to maiden and to boy,
And fashioned by the gods for our annoy.

from the Greek
Mimnermus
G. Lowes Dickinson

Lovely as a flower,
So pure, so fair, thou art;
When I see thee, sorrow
Steals into my heart.

I feel I ought above thy head
To lift my hands in prayer,
Then the Lord may keep thee
So lovely, pure, and fair.

from the German
Heinrich Heine
Kate Flores

sing

a song

of seasons

Rondeau

The year his winter cloak lets fall;
Wind, snow and rain, he lays them by,
And dons the shining broidery
Of lucid sunlight, gilding all.
The birds and beasts, both great and small,
Do in their jargon sing or cry:
The year his winter cloak lets fall;
Wind, snow and rain, he lays them by.
River and brook and waterfall
Wear, for a sparkling livery,
Their gold and silver jewelry;
All deck them for high festival.
The year his winter cloak lets fall.

from the French
Charles d'Orléans
J. G. Legge

If it were not for the voice
Of the nightingale,
How would the mountain-village
Where the snow is still unmelted
Know the spring?

from the Japanese
Shūi Shū
Arthur Waley

The Gusts of Winter Are Gone

The gusts of winter are gone; the sky no longer lowers,
Spring with her smiles is here, Spring with her purple flowers.
The dark earth crowns herself with grassy chaplets green.
The blooming woods are tressed with leafage of new sheen.
The meadows all do laugh with bursting of the rose—
Drenched with the quickening dew, at dawn their buds unclose.

The shepherd's heart is glad, his clear pipe wakes the hill.
The little frisking kids with joy the goatherds thrill.
Over the wide sea-waves fearless the shipmen sail,
Their bellying canvas filled with Zephyr's harmless gale.
Once more with ivy flowers their locks the feasters twine
And shout, "Hail! Bacchus, hail! thou giver of the vine!"
Busy about the hive, the bees with cunning skill
The fair white waxen comb with newdript honey fill.
On all sides round the birds do sound with their jargon shrill—
The halcyon over the waves, the swallow about the eaves,
The swan on the river's shore, the nightingale in the leaves.
If then the earth is gay, and the trees of the wood rejoice,
And the shepherd joys in his pipe and the flocks at the shep-
    herd's voice,
And the sea is alive with ships and the shore with the dancers'
    feet,
And the air with the song of bird and drone of bee, 'tis meet
That the poet too with song the coming of Spring should greet.

from the Greek
Meleager
L. P. Chamberlayne

Recall how with frozen fingers December's clouds outspread
Over the fields and uplands a mantle of ice and snow;
Over the buried roses, over a world of dead
Vengeful as any hangman stalked the exultant crow.

But lo, the abiding wonder! Spirit, that never dies,
Surges anew and vital through the upstanding trees.
See, those spear-armed horsemen, the spreading tulips, rise
Over the plains triumphant, hills, yea, and mountains seize.
Behold, the eager lily leaps to delight the eye,
Spurning the bent narcissus crouched in his self-regard.
Deep in the springing corn-shoots the gleaming violets lie;
Bright with a myriad jewels the wheat-swept fields are starred.
Under the nodding willow the poppy lies in blood—
Sudden the blow that smote her, drenched her in crimson flood.
And now, 'mid the green profusion of wheat, in mingled hue
Note how the lily argent with lily azure glows;
So, when the sky is stippled with scattered rain-clouds through
Here and here betwixt them the vault of heaven shows.

from the Persian
Bahar
A. J. Arberry

The good rain knows when to fall,
Coming in this spring to help the seeds,
Choosing to fall by night with a friendly wind,
Silently moistening the whole earth.
Over this silent wilderness the clouds are dark.
The only light shines from a river boat.
Tomorrow morning everything will be red and wet,
And all Chengtu will be covered with blossoming flowers.

from the Chinese
Tu Fu
Anonymous

Clearing at Dawn

The fields are chill, the sparse rain has stopped;
The colours of Spring teem on every side.
With leaping fish the blue pond is full;
With singing thrushes the green boughs droop.
The flowers of the field have dabbled their powdered cheeks;
The mountain grasses are bent level at the waist.
By the bamboo stream the last fragment of cloud
Blown by the wind slowly scatters away.

from the Chinese
Li T'ai-po
Arthur Waley

Alons au Bois le May Cueillir

We'll to the woods and gather may
Fresh from the footprints of the rain;
   We'll to the woods, at every vein
To drink the spirit of the day.
The winds of the spring are out at play,
   The needs of spring in heart and brain.
We'll to the woods and gather may
   Fresh from the footprints of the rain.

The world's too near her end, you say?—
   Hark to the blackbird's mad refrain.
   It waits for her, the vast Inane?—
Then, girls, to help her on the way
We'll to the woods and gather may.

from the French
Charles d'Orléans
W. E. Henley

Song

On the Eastern Way at the City of Lo-yang
At the edge of the road peach-trees and plum-trees grow;
On the two sides,—flower matched by flower;
Across the road,—leaf touching leaf.

A spring wind rises from the north-east;
Flowers and leaves gently nod and sway.
Up the road somebody's daughter comes
Carrying a basket, to gather silkworms' food.

> *(She sees the fruit trees in blossom and,*
> *forgetting about her silkworms, begins to*
> *pluck the branches.)*

With her slender hand she breaks a branch from the tree;
The flowers fall, tossed and scattered in the wind.

> *The tree says:*

"Lovely lady, I never did you harm;
Why should you hate me and do me injury?"

> *The lady answers:*

"At high autumn in the eighth and ninth moons
When the white dew changes to hoar-frost,
At the year's end the wind would have lashed your boughs,
Your sweet fragrance could not have lasted long.
Though in the autumn your leaves patter to the ground,
When spring comes, your gay bloom returns.
But in men's lives when their bright youth is spent
Joy and love never come back again."

from the Chinese
Sung Tzŭ-hou
Arthur Waley

In the season of Spring is the season of growing;
  Where lies the inviolate orchard-meadow,
    The apple-garden where Maidens dwell,
There, watered freshly with runnels flowing,
    The quince-trees blossom, and safe in shadow
      The vine-buds under the vine-leaf swell
In the season of Spring. But in my heart passion
    At no tide ever asleep is laid:
From the Lady of Love as a blast of the North,
When a blaze of lightning flashes it forth,
    With a rush, with a burst,
In a dark storm parching and maddening with thirst,
    Unabashed, unafraid,
It shoots to my bosom, gripping it still
    In the same rude fashion,
And shakes and shatters at will.

from the Greek
Ibycus
Walter Headlam

Wild Geese

Where bright waters flood the Spring shore
A journeying flock swerves with bended wing;
They sip the wavelets, tug the yielding wing;
Their folded wings flaked with icy dew,
A-flock they sail, pushing the quiet stream,
Or singly each his own gleam pursues.
Now almost earthward they trail a dipping flight;
Now upward quavering tumbled legions rise.
Each rushing wing skims the rippled lake;
At one swoop they are gone to their native land.

from the Chinese
Shēn Yo
Arthur Waley

The Little Valley in Spring

A mountain stream:
even the stones make songs—
wild cherry trees.

from the Japanese
Onitsura
Harold G. Henderson

The earth is sweet with roses,
And rich with marigold,
And violets and crocus
Are wet with running streams. . . .

And through the grassy meadows,
The blessed spirits go,
Their white feet shod with lilies,
And as they go they sing.

from the Latin (Medieval)
Prudentius
Helen Waddell

In Spring

I lie here on the hill of spring;
The cloud becomes my wing;
A bird flies away at my feet.
Ah tell me, all-singular love,
Where you take rest that with you I may stay;
But you and the breezes, you have no retreat.

My spirit like the sunflower stands wide open,
Yearning,
Out-turning
In loving and hoping.
Spring, what goads you, possessed?
When shall I be at rest?
I watch the motion of the cloud and stream;
The golden kiss of the sunbeam
Into my heart's blood pierces deep;
My eyes, by potent lethargies
Sung shut, might seem asleep,
But the ear catches still the sound of bees.

I think of this and think of that,
I long, and do not rightly know for what,
Half it delights me, half dismays;
Say, heart, O phrase,
What recollection do you weave
Out of dawn mist the gold-green branches leave?
Old, unnamable days!

from the German
Eduard Mörike
Vernon Watkins

A fluttering swarm
Of cherry-petals;—and there comes,
Pursuing them, the storm!

from the Japanese
Sadaiye
Harold G. Henderson

Pear-Trees by the Fence

Pear-trees translucent white;
  (My heart is sad to-night).
Willows brilliant green;
  (Against the rail I lean).
Catkins and pearly blossoms fill the air.

The pear-tree by the fence
  (How soon we must go hence!)
Is a pillar of snow.
  (A man may never know
How few springs such as this will be his share!)

from the Chinese
Su Tung-p'o
E. D. Edwards

Swiftly the years, beyond recall.
Solemn the stillness of this fair morning.
I will clothe myself in spring-clothing
And visit the slopes of the Eastern Hill.
By the mountain-stream a mist hovers,
Hovers a moment, then scatters.
There comes a wind blowing from the south
That brushes the fields of new corn.

from the Chinese
T'ao Ch'ien
Arthur Waley

On the Road to Nara

Oh, these spring days!
A nameless little mountain,
wrapped in morning haze!

from the Japanese
Matsuo Bashō
Harold G. Henderson

The sun's way:
  hollyhocks turn toward it
    through all the rain of May.

from the Japanese
Matsuo Bashō
Harold G. Henderson

from Carmina Burana

O Spring the long-desired,
  The lover's hour!
O flaming torch of joy,
  Sap of each flower,
    All hail!
O jocund company
  Of many flowers,
O many-coloured light,
  All hail,
And foster our delight!
The birds sing out in chorus.
O youth, joy is before us,
Cold winter has passed on,
And the Spring winds are come!

The earth's aflame again
  With flowers bright,
The fields are green again,
  The shadows deep,
Woods are in leaf again,
There is no living thing
That is not gay again.
  With face of light
  Garbed with delight,
    Love is reborn.
And Beauty wakes from sleep.

                    from the Latin (Medieval)
                         Anonymous
                      Helen Waddell

Summer Night

  A lightning flash:
    between the forest trees
    I have seen water.

                      from the Japanese
                           Shiki
                    Harold G. Henderson

Now ripened berries fill
The forest clearing's lap.
Sternly the fir trees watch
Over the valley's nap.

Bright scarlet strawberry juice
Has stained the reindeer's lips;
While, in his antlers caught,
A bluebell swings and dips.

from the Russian
Lyudmila Tatyanicheva
Babette Deutsch

In the summer palace the fireflies have lost their way. The sky
    is like water.
The bamboos are yellow, the pond cold, the water lilies dead.
Speechless the moon shines on the gold rings of the gate.
Beyond the cool courtyard and the empty hall lies a white sky.
A hurrying wind has strewn the frost flowers.
Brocades of dappled emerald are piled on the road.
The cock herald crows no more, dawn flows like diamonds
    and jade.
Above the gold well croaks a raven. The leaves of the plane
    tree fall.

from the Chinese
Li Ho
Ho Chih-yuan

Maple Leaves

    Envied by us all,
        turning to such loveliness—
        red leaves that fall.

from the Japanese
Shikō
Harold G. Henderson

When a sighing begins
In the violins
Of the autumn-song,
My heart is drowned
In the slow sound
Languorous and long.

Pale as with pain,
Breath fails me when
The hour tolls deep.
My thoughts recover
The days that are over,
And I weep.

And I go
Where the winds know,
Broken and brief,
To and fro,
As the winds blow
A dead leaf.

from the French
Paul Verlaine
Arthur Symons

The leaves fall, fall as from far,
Like distant gardens withered in the heavens;
They fall with slow and lingering descent.

And in the nights the heavy Earth, too, falls
From out the stars into the Solitude.

Thus all doth fall. This hand of mine must fall,
And lo! the other one:—it is the law.
But there is One who holds this falling
Infinitely softly in His hands.

from the German
Rainer Maria Rilke
Jessie Lemont

Parting

    For me who go,
      for you who stay—
    two autumns.

from the Japanese
Buson
Harold G. Henderson

I shall not miss the roses, fading
As soon as spring's fleet days are done;
I love the grapes whose clusters ripen
Upon the hillsides in the sun—
The glory of my fertile valley,
They hang, each lustrous as a pearl,
Gold autumn's joy, oblong, transparent,
Like the slim fingers of a girl.

from the Russian
Alexander Pushkin
Avrahm Yarmolinsky

The White Egret

A solitary egret, left behind
In the swift southward flight,
Sinks like a falling snowflake on the river;
Not ready yet to fly, it rests awhile
Beside a sandbank, motionless.
No fears ruffle its white breast, smooth as the water
From which the ripple of its coming has withdrawn.

from the Chinese
Li Po
E. D. Edwards

The Cranes

The western wind has blown but a few days;
Yet the first leaf already flies from the bough.
On the drying paths I walk in my thin shoes;
In the first cold I have donned my quilted coat.
Through shallow ditches the floods are clearing away;
Through sparse bamboos trickles a slanting light.
In the early dusk, down an alley of green moss,
The garden-boy is leading the cranes home.

from the Chinese
Po Chü-i
Arthur Waley

On a Mountain Road

Clouds on the mountain
Are hanging low;
The path, winding upward,
Is lost to view.
Cold autumn breezes
Blow through my gown;
Monkeys call sadly;
The sun goes down.

from the Chinese
Wu Ch'ing-jen
E. D. Edwards

In the clear cold the dales grow blue and tremble;
The iron hoofs beat sharply, knock on knock.
The faded grasses in wide skirts assemble
Flung copper where the wind-blown willows rock.

From empty glens, a slender arch ascending,
Fog curls upon the air and mosswise grows,
While evening, low above the river bending,
In its white waters washes his blue toes.

> from the Russian
> *Sergey Yesenin*
> Babette Deutsch

A Snowy Day

I cannot sleep or take the air—
Of a truth this load is hard to bear!
Ford or slope is none to be found,
Nor open space, nor bare ground.
No girl's word shall tempt me now
Out of my house into the snow.

The plaguey feathers drifting down
Like dragon's scales cling to the gown,
And all I wear would soon be
White as miller's coat to see.
True 'tis, the Winter Calends gone,
Ermine's the wear for everyone;
In January's month, first of the year,
God makes hermits everywhere.
Everywhere, the country round,
He has whitewashed the black ground,
Clothed in white each woodland glade,
On every copse a white sheet spread.
To every stump clings heavenly meal,
Like the white blossoms of April.
A cold veil on the forest lies,
A load of chalk crushes the trees.
Like wheaten flour the drifts appear,
A coat of mail that the plains wear,
A cold grit on field and fallow,
On earth's whole skin a thick tallow,
Foam-flakes flying thick and fast,
Fleeces big as a man's fist,
White bees of heaven on the wing,
Through all Gwynedd wandering.
Will God's plenty never cease—
So many feathers of holy geese,
Like winnowed chaff, heaped together,
A robe of ermine above the heather?

There in deep drifts the fine dust stays,
Where song was and the winding ways.
Who can tell me what folk they are
On the wintry earth spit from afar?
Heaven's white angels they must be
Busy about their carpentry.
The plank is lifted from the flour bin,
And down floats the flour within;
Silver cloaks of ice that pass,
Quicksilver, the coldest ever was,
A hampering chimer, white and chill,
Cement on hollow, ditch, and hill,
Earth's mail corselet, cold and hard,
A pavement vast as the sea's graveyard.
On all my land what monstrous fall,
From sea to sea a gray wall!
Who dare affront its rude domain?
A cloak of lead!—where is the rain?

from the Welsh
Dafydd Ap Gwilym
H. Idris Bell

A magic landscape,
My heart's delight:
A full moon's brightness,
A plain sheer white,

The high sky lighted,
The snow's pure ray,
And far-off gliding,
A lonely sleigh.

from the Russian
Afanasy Fet
Babette Deutsch

Winter

Mountains and plains,
    all are captured by the snow—
        nothing remains.

from the Japanese
Jōsō
Harold G. Henderson

Now the sweet-voiced nightingale
In the woods takes up her tale,
Itys, Itys her refrain,
Waking grief to light again.
Shepherds on the hilly weald
Pipe their reeds to flocks afield;
Yellow foals in couples pass,
Roused from stall to eat their grass;
And the huntsman sets to work
Quartering where the wild beasts lurk.
Swans about the Ocean springs
Cry, and sweet their music rings;
Boats cast off and take the seas
Driven by oar and spanking breeze;
Sails, run up to catch the blow,
Bellying white to fore-stay go.

from the Greek
Euripides
Anonymous

O Sun, when I stand in my green leaves,
  With my petals full of dew,
And you fare forth in your splendor,
  My blossoming heart looks to you.
When, on the red dawn throning,
  The world at your feet you view,
Forget not the little flower
  That waits and watches for you!

O Sun, you that climb never tired
  The lofty paths of the skies,
My leaves, that open to see you,
  Follow you as you rise. . . .
Come and seek out my heart and find it,
  For you it lives and dies!
It waits for you, it loves you . . .
  O my Bridegroom from Paradise!

And when in the evening the dark comes,
  When you haste to the welcoming West,
I watch your last beams fading,
  I see you sink down to rest.

With my head bowed I weep till the morning,
      Forsaken and distressed.
   Come back, my Beloved, I am waiting
      To rise up and be caressed!

from the Flemish
Guido Gezelle
Jethro Bithell

Lotus Leaves

      Over the lotus leaves
      A refreshing shower has run;
   Now, on the white jewels of dew
      The splendour of the setting sun!

from the Japanese
Mitsukuni
Miyamori Asataro

Dove-colored, the shadows melt and mingle,
Color fades and sound has gone to sleep;
Motion is dissolved in distant rumours,
Undulant the dark, with life at neap. . . .
Beating the nocturnal air, a night moth
Is in flight, softly, invisibly. . . .
Hour of unutterable longing!
I am in the all, the all in me.

Gentle twilight, slumber-lidded twilight.
Brim my being with your quietness,
Let your silent, tender, fragrant languor
Rise in flood to tranquillize and bless.
Give my senses over to the darkness
Of pure self-forgetfulness to keep.
Let me taste annihilation, mix me
With the universe that lies asleep.

from the Russian
Fyodor Tyutchev
Babette Deutsch

Beauty is most at twilight's close.
All the love the heavens dispose
Hovers aglimmer, agloom
Over the fields,
Over the earth house-strewn.

All is tenderness, all is caressed by hands.
The Lord himself blots out the distant lands.
All near, all far.
On loan to man
Are given all things that are.

All is mine, and all shall be taken from me,
In a little while all shall be taken from me.
Trees, clouds, the ground I pace.
I shall fare alone—
Nor track nor trace.

from the Swedish
Pär Lagerkvist
G. Kenneth Laycock

Softly the day dies out behind the pines;
  Over the heathland still the red light blazes;
But paler now and paler the sun shines
  On the thin pastures dotted o'er with daisies.

The plain is vast. The mists of evening lie
  Spread at the verge in veils that shift and shimmer;
Yonder a tree uprears to the azure sky
  Its leaves that in the twilight faintly glimmer.

Now listen! Not a sound stirs far and wide.
  The birds are silent in their leafy cover;
Only a cricket chirps by the way-side,
  And ghostly breezes o'er the landscape hover.

Slowly, as though afraid of her own feet
  On the parched grass, the shepherdess is leading
Home to the fold her flock too tired to bleat,
  Red in the light the dying sun is bleeding.

from the Flemish
Pol de Mont
Jethro Bithell

Nightfall. The coolness of my watered garden.
Between the great green leaves, the setting sun
sends a yellow farewell, pressed by an
enormous leaden cloud, purple and taciturn.

The flowers still are dripping the raindrops of late rain;
some clear mouths of silver sing in another part;
there is vague desire, sensuous and immense,
of love-closed eyes and half-opened lips.

A momentary light comes pushing out the dark;
the grasses and the roses are fragrant as in dreams;
the window becomes fiery and fashions for the fountain
a broken quiver, a melodious swelling of gold.

from the Spanish
Juan Ramón Jiménez
Eloise Roach

I wander through the silent night;
The moon slips secret, soft, and bright
Oft from its darkening cloudy cover.
And now along the vale
Wakens the nightingale
Till a gray hush again spreads over.

O wonder-filled nocturnal song,
Far hidden waters whisper long,
Trees shiver as the moonlight gleams—
Under the spell you cast
My wandering song is lost
And like a calling-out of dreams.

from the German
Joseph von Eichendorff
Herman Salinger

Night

An odorous shade lingers the fair day's ghost,
   And the frail moon now by no wind is tost,
And shadow-laden scents of tree and grass
   Build up again a world our eyes have lost.

Now all the wood is but a murmured light
   Where leaf on leaf falls softly from the height;
The hidden freshness of the river seems
   A breath that mingles with the breath of night.

And time and shade and silence seem to say,
   Close now your eyes nor fear to die with day;
For if the daylight win to earth again,
   Will not its beauty also find a way?

And flower and stream and forest, will they not
   Bring back to-morrow, as to-day they brought,
This shadow-hidden scent—this odorous shade?
   Yea, and with more abiding memories fraught.

from the French
Henri de Regnier
Seumas O'Sullivan

It were as if the heavens
The earth had quietly kissed,
That she, midst shimmering blossoms,
Now dream of heaven must.

The breeze passed through the corn fields,
The ears made movements slight,
The forest rustled gently,
So star-clear was the night.

My soul stretched forth her pinions,
And spread them wide to roam,
Flew through the silent landscapes
As if she flew toward home.

from the German
Joseph von Eichendorff
Mabel Cotterell

When its rays fall on its cheeks the cat licks them, thinking
　　them milk;
When they are caught in the cleft of a tree the elephant deems
　　them a lotus;
When they rest on the couch of lovers the maiden seizes them,
　　saying, " 'Tis my robe";
The moon in truth, proud of its brilliance, doth lead astray all
　　this world.

from the Sanskrit
Bhasa
A. Berriedale Keith

The New and the Old

Railroad tracks; a flight
of wild geese close above
in the moonlit night.

from the Japanese
Shiki
Harold G. Henderson

charm me asleep

What little throat
Has framed that note?
What gold beak shot
   It far away?
A blackbird on
His leafy throne
Tossed it alone
   Across the bay.

from the Irish
Anonymous
Frank O'Connor

With wavering feet I walked where dawn-lit mists were lying,
To find the shores of wonder and of mystery.
Dawn struggled with the final stars, frail dreams were flying,
While unto unknown gods my morning lips were crying
The prayers that my dream-imprisoned soul had whispered me.

The noon is cold and candid, the road winds on severely,
And through an unknown land once more my journey lies.
The mist has lifted now, and the bare eye sees clearly
How hard the mountain road that rises upward sheerly,
How distant looms the dream the prescient heart descries.

Yet onward with unfaltering feet I shall be going
Till midnight, onward toward the shore of my desires,
Where, on a mountain height, new stars its glory showing,
My promised temple waits, with plinth and pillar glowing,
Beaten about with flames of white, triumphal fires.

from the Russian
Vladimir Solovyov
Babette Deutsch

Where shall we dance in a circle?
shall it be on the shores of the sea?
The sea will dance with its thousand waves,
an orange-flower garland free.

Shall it be at the foot of the mountains?
Each mount will an answer fling,
as if all the stones of all the world
were longing at heart to sing.

Shall it be in the depths of the forest?
Its voices will blend, in bliss;
the songs of children and songs of birds
in the wind will meet and kiss.

We will dance in an infinite circle;
in the woods we will weave it with glee;
we will dance at the foot of the mountains,
and on all the shores of the sea.

from the Spanish
Gabriela Mistral
Alice Stone Blackwell

Awake! for Morning in the Bowl of Night
Has flung the Stone that puts the Stars to Flight:
   And Lo! the Hunter of the East has caught
The Sultán's Turret in a Noose of Light.

. . .

Come, fill the Cup, and in the Fire of Spring
The Winter Garment of Repentance fling:
   The Bird of Time has but a little way
To fly—and Lo! the Bird is on the Wing.

. . .

Here with a Loaf of Bread beneath the Bough,
A Flask of Wine, A Book of Verse—and Thou
   Beside me singing in the Wilderness—
And Wilderness is Paradise enow.

. . .

Think, in this batter'd Caravanserai
Whose Doorways are alternate Night and Day,
   How Sultán after Sultán with his Pomp
Abode his Hour or two, and went his way.

. . .

I sometimes think that never blows so red
The rose as where some buried Caesar bled;
   That every Hyacinth the Garden wears
Dropt in its Lap from some once lovely Head.

And this delightful Herb whose tender Green
Fledges the River's Lip on which we lean—
　　Ah, lean upon it lightly! for who knows
From what once lovely Lip it springs unseen!

Ah, my Belovéd, fill the Cup that clears
TO-DAY of past Regrets and future Fears—
　　To-morrow?—Why, To-morrow I may be
Myself with Yesterday's Sev'n Thousand Years.

Lo! some we loved, the loveliest and the best
That Time and Fate of all their Vintage prest,
　　Have drunk their Cup a Round or two before,
And one by one crept silently to Rest.

　　　　　.　　.　　.

Ah, fill the Cup:—what boots it to repeat
How Time is slipping underneath our Feet:
　　Unborn TO-MORROW, and dead YESTERDAY
Why fret about them if TO-DAY be sweet!

　　　　　.　　.　　.

Alas, that Spring should vanish with the Rose!
That Youth's sweet-scented Manuscript should close!
　　The Nightingale that in the Branches sang,
Ah, whence, and whither flown again, who knows!

Ah, Love! could thou and I with Fate conspire
To grasp this sorry Scheme of Things entire,
    Would not we shatter it to bits—and then
Re-mould it nearer to the Heart's Desire!

Ah, Moon of my Delight, who know'st no wane,
The Moon of Heav'n is rising once again:
    How oft hereafter rising shall she look
Through this same Garden after me—in vain!

And when Thyself with shining Foot shall pass
Among the Guests Star-scatter'd on the Grass,
    And in thy joyous Errand reach the Spot
Where I made one—turn down an empty Glass!

from the Persian
Omar Khayyám
Edward FitzGerald

Be silent, secret, and conceal
Whatever you may think or feel.
The dreams your spirit knows should move
As soundlessly as far above
Do stars on their nocturnal route:
Admire them, watch them, and be mute.

How can a heart at will unfold
Its tale? Can anyone be told
The truth by which you live and die?
A thought when uttered is a lie.
The springs men dig for they pollute:
Drink secret waters, and be mute.

Within yourself know how to live.
Magic that is not fugitive
Waits, a possession of the mind,
Thoughts that the glare of day will blind
And noisy busyness confute:
Heed that hushed music, and be mute.

from the Russian
Fyodor Tyutchev
Babette Deutsch

As ocean holds the globe in its embrace,
So dreams about our earthly life are sweeping;
Night comes, and the sonorous billows chase
Each other, on the coast of darkness leaping.

That voice of dream, how urgently it sounds!
Alert, the magic skiff prepares to wander;
The tide swells swiftly, now the white sail rounds,
And we are borne to shoreless waters yonder.

Lo, the high heavens, starred and luminous,
Mysteriously from the deeps are gazing,
And we sail onward, while surrounding us
On every side the strange abyss is blazing.

from the Russian
Fyodor Tyutchev
Babette Deutsch

Knowest thou the land where bloom the lemon trees,
And darkly gleam the golden oranges?
A gentle wind blows down from that blue sky;
Calm stands the myrtle and the laurel high.
Knowest thou the land? So far and fair!
Thou, whom I love, and I will wander there.

Knowest thou the house with all its rooms aglow,
And shining hall and columned portico?
The marble statues stand and look at me.
Alas, poor child, what have they done to thee?
Knowest thou the land? So far and fair.
My guardian, thou and I will wander there.

Knowest thou the mountain with its bridge of cloud?
The mule plods warily: the white mists crowd.
Coiled in their caves the brood of dragons sleep;
The torrent hurls the rock from steep to steep.
Knowest thou the land? So far and fair.
Father, away! Our road is over there!

from the German
Johann Wolfgang von Goethe
James Elroy Flecker

Splashing water,
Luscious grass;
Somebody's child is herding an ox,
Riding his ox by the river-side.
Browsing ox,
Happy youth;
Somebody's child is singing a song,
Shouting his song to a little white cloud:

Away at morn my ox I ride,
And back again at eventide.

My two feet never touch the dust;
In wealth and fame who puts his trust?

My rush hat shelters me from rain;
In silk and sables what's to gain?

I quench my thirst at a mountain rill;
Who'd spend a fortune his belly to fill?

When the sun on his golden horse rides high
Down by the river go ox and I;

When the sinking sun makes shadows creep
He carries me home on his back, asleep.

from the Chinese
Chen Shan-min
E. D. Edwards

A Garden

Cool waters tumble, singing as they go
  Through appled boughs. Softly the leaves are dancing.
Down streams a slumber on the drowsy flow,
  My soul entrancing.

from the Greek
Sappho
T. F. Higham

Coolness

  How cool the breeze:
    the sky is filled with voices—
      pine and cedar trees.

from the Japanese
Onitsura
Harold G. Henderson

Yellow butterflies
Over the blossoming virgin corn,
  With pollen-painted faces
Chase one another in brilliant throng.

Blue butterflies
Over the blossoming virgin beans,
  With pollen-painted faces
Chase one another in brilliant streams.

Over the blossoming corn,
Over the virgin corn
Wild bees hum;
Over the blossoming corn,
Over the virgin beans
Wild bees hum.

Over your field of growing corn
All day shall hang the thunder-cloud;
Over your field of growing corn
All day shall come the rushing rain.

from the Hopi (American Indian)
Anonymous
Natalie Curtis

The tree frogs sing:
and on the young leaves, suddenly
a raindrop-pattering.

from the Japanese
Rogetsu
Harold G. Henderson

Your flute,
    you fashioned it from the shin of a mighty bull
    and you polished it on the arid hillsides
    scourged by the sun;
    his flute,
    he fashioned it from a quivering reed in the breeze
    and he pierced it at the brink of running waters
    drunk with the dreams of the moon.

You play your flutes together in the depths of the evening,
    as if to hold back the spherical canoe
    which capsizes at the banks of the heavens;
    as if to deliver it
    from its fate;
    but your plaintive songs,
    are they heard by the gods of the winds,
    of the earth and of the forest,
    and of the sand?

Your flute
    draws out a note charged with the stamp of a raging bull
    which runs to the waste-lands
    and returns at a run,
    scorched by thirst and hunger,
    but felled with fatigue

at the foot of a tree that is shadeless,
fruitless, leafless.
His flute
is like a pliant reed
bending 'neath the weight of a bird of passage—
not a bird caught by a child
with ruffled feathers,
but a bird far from his own kin
watching his shadow, to seek consolation,
on the running water.

Your flute
and his—
mourn for their origins
in the songs of your sorrows.

from the French (Madagascar)
Jean-Joseph Rabéarivelo
Dorothy Blair

Come sit aneath this pinetree, whose lofty tressèd crown
    Sighs as her tufty sprays stir to the west wind's kiss:
And with the babbling waters my flute thy care shall drown,
    And lull thy dreamy eyelids to sweet forgetful bliss.

from the Greek
Plato
Robert Bridges

The Bird

Though the evening comes with slow steps and has signalled
    for all songs to cease;
Though your companions have gone to their rest and you are
    tired;
Though fear broods in the dark and the face of the sky is veiled;
Yet, bird, O my bird, listen to me, do not close your wings.

That is not the gloom of the leaves of the forest, that is the sea
    swelling like a dark black smoke.
That is not the dance of the flowering jasmine, that is flashing
    foam.
Ah, where is the sunny green shore, where is your nest?
Bird, O my bird, listen to me, do not close your wings.

The lone night lies along your path, the dawn sleeps behind the
shadowy hills.
The stars hold their breath counting the hours, the feeble moon
swims the deep night.
Bird, O my bird, listen to me, do not close your wings.

There is no hope, no fear for you.
There is no word, no whisper, no cry.
There is no home, no bed of rest.
There is only your own pair of wings and the pathless sky.
Bird, O my bird, listen to me, do not close your wings.

from the Sanskrit
Rabindranath Tagore
Rabindranath Tagore

Plover, my lover, how lightly you hover
The water over!
Gracefully darting and skimming, what time the rivers are
    brimming.
Oh! lovely, lovely bird—bright eyes and crested head!
All night I lie awake till dawn comes up red,
Thinking of your white wings, beloved, O Plover!

> from the Swahili (African)
> *Anonymous*
> Dr. Alice Werner

Serenade

Harken how the flute complains,
And the fountains plash and glisten!
Music drifts in golden rains;
Softly, softly let us listen!
Gentle-pleading, mild desire
Sweetly tells the heart its plight!
Through the darkness, bright as fire,
Gleams upon me—music's light.

> from the German
> *Clemens Brentano*
> Herman Salinger

On music drawn away, a sea-borne mariner
 Star over bowsprit pale,
Beneath a roof of mist or depths of lucid air
 I put out under sail;

Breastbone my steady bow and lungs full, running free
 Before a following gale,
I ride the rolling back and mass of every sea
 By Night wrapt in her veil;

All passions and all joys that vessels undergo
 Tremble alike in me;
Fair winds or waves in havoc when the tempests blow
 On the enormous sea
Rock me, and level calms come silvering sea and air,
 A glass for my despair.

from the French
Charles Baudelaire
Robert Fitzgerald

We are such stuff as dreams are made of, and these
Our dreams do open such ecstatic eyes
As little children under cherry trees,

Upon whose crowns the risen full moon lies,
Bound through the great night on her voyaging.
. . . Not otherwise do these our dreams arise,

Are there and live, as a child's laugh will ring,
And not less great, as up and down they strive,
Than the full moon on trees awakening.

Into the inmost hiding-place they drive,
As spirit hands within a locked space gleam
They are in us and always are alive.

And three are one: a man, a thing, a dream.

from the German
Hugo von Hofmannsthal
Jethro Bithell

I know not what I seek eternally
on earth, in air, and sky;
I know not what I seek; but it is something
that I have lost, I know not when,
and cannot find, although in dreams invisibly
it dwells in all I touch and see.

Ah, bliss! Never can I recapture you
either on earth, in air, or sky,
although I know you have reality
and are no futile dream!

from the Spanish
Rosalía de Castro
Muriel Kittel

There calleth me ever a marvelous Horn,
   "Come away! Come away!"
Is it earthly music faring astray,
   Or is it air-born?
Oh, whether it be a spirit-wile
   Or a forest voice,
It biddeth mine ailing heart rejoice,
   Yet sorrow the while!

In the greenwood glades—o'er the garlanded bowl—
   Night, Noontide, and Morn,
The summoning call of that marvelous Horn
   Tones home to my soul!
In vain have I sought for it east and west,
   But I darkly feel
That so soon as its music shall cease to peal
   I go to my rest!

from the German
Justinus Kerner
James Clarence Mangan

1

The voice that beautifies the land!
The voice above,
The voice of the thunder,
Among the dark clouds
Again and again it sounds,
The voice that beautifies the land.

2

The voice that beautifies the land!
The voice below,
The voice of the grasshopper,
Among the flowers and grasses
Again and again it sounds,
The voice that beautifies the land.

from the Navaho (American Indian)
Anonymous
Washington Matthews

Roaring Wind, soaring Wind,
Leaping the skies,
Tell me where your homeland lies.

"Child, we've been blowing
Years, years beyond all knowing
Round the wide, the wide old world,
That same question crying,
Demanding a replying,
Asking the mountains, seas, and coasts,
Asking the heaven's sounding hosts,
And not one could say!
If you're wiser than they
We would learn it of you!
But onward, away!
Bid us not stay!
Behind us there are coming others,
Ask our brothers!"

Wind, not so fast!
A moment stay!
Where has Love its homeland, say!
Where do its frontiers run?

"Who can name it? None!
Listen, roguish child,
Love's like the wind—as wild,
Swift, and life-giving;
Resting never,
She lives forever,
Yet fugitive still in her living.
But onward, away!
Bid us not stay!
Away over forest and stubble and meadow!
If thy sweetheart I see
I'll kiss her for thee!
Good-by, little fellow!"

from the German
Eduard Mörike
William R. Hughes

Oh, I should love to be like one of those
Who thro' the night on tameless horses ride,
With torches like disheveled tresses wide
Which the great wind of gallop streaming blows.
And I would stand as on a shallop's prow,
Slender and tall and like a banner rolled.
Dark but for helmeting of ruddy gold
That glints and gleams. Behind me in a row
Ten men who from the equal darkness glow
With helmets of the changeful gold designed,
Now clear as glass, now dark and old and blind.
And one by me blows me a vision of space
Upon a trumpet glittering that cries,
Or makes a solitary blackness rise
Thro' which as in a rapid dream we race:
The houses slant behind us to their knees,
The crooked streets to meet us bend and strain,
The squares flee from us: but we grapple these,
And still our horses rustle like the rain.

from the German
Rainer Maria Rilke
Ludwig Lewisohn

The white moon
Gleams in the wood;
From every branch
There comes a voice
Beneath the bower . . .

O my love.

The pond reflects,
Shimmering mirror,
The silhouette
Of the dim willow
Where the wind laments . . .

Let us dream, it is the hour.

Vast and tender
An appeasement
Seems to lower
From the firmament
Star-bedecked . . .

Exquisite hour.

from the French
Paul Verlaine
Kate Flores

The moldering hulk
of the old sloop
rests upon the sand . . .
The tattered sail seems still
To be dreaming upon the sun and the sea.

The sea bubbles and sings . . .
The sea is a sonorous dream
under the April sun.
The sea bubbles and laughs
with azure waves and foam of milk and silver,
the sea bubbles and laughs
under the azure sky.
The milky sea,
the glittering sea,
laughing its azure laughter upon its silver lyres . . .
It bubbles and laughs, the sea! . . .

The wind seems to be sleeping entranced
in the lambent haze of the bleaching sun.
A gull hovers in the dormant air, and in slow,
drowsy flight drifts away and is lost amid the mist of the sun.

from the Spanish
Antonio Machado
Kate Flores

Looking at the Moon and Thinking of One Far Away

The moon, grown full now over the sea,
Brightening the whole of heaven,
Brings to separated hearts
The long thoughtfulness of night. . . .
It is no darker though I blow out my candle.
It is no warmer though I put on my coat.
So I leave my message with the moon
And turn to my bed, hoping for dreams.

from the Chinese
Chang Chiu-ling
Witter Bynner

The Sea

Blue drifted the sea; the waters of the sun
Flowed fresh from out the golden fount and ran
On woolly waves that with its cleansing flash
Anointed were. From open hollows dashed
Waves up like white-wooled rams, all thoroughbreds
With tress of foam and horns upon their heads.

146 But on its edge the sea broke ceaselessly
     In reef on reef, and clouds above the sea
     Drifted like golden bees along the blue.
     Thousands of tiny mouths blew drops of dew
     And salt in pellets on the lips of each
     Crimson-mouthed shell, the flowers of the beach,
     White ones and creamy yellow, and others red
     Like babies' nails and striped and blue as lead,
     Like an evening sky that's tippled by the breeze.
     And there were conches that murmured melodies
     Quietly. And high above the wave's deep ring,
     A clearer note, just as wet vowels sing
     In the dry word. The sea shells tinkled in
     The glittering water, glass, gravel, and tin,
     Metallic rings. And water bubbles swollen
     With music, light, on feathery wing, like pollen,
     Were borne by lighter wind. Across the dune
     They floated through the air, laden with tune,
     Into the polder, and the fullest one
     Sank, burst, and scattered music clearer than
     The song of voices and, in glad surprise,
     Each dune looked up from dreamy memories.

from the Dutch
Herman Gorter
A. J. Barnouw

In the blossom-land Japan
Somewhere thus an old song ran.

Said a warrior to a smith
"Hammer me a sword forthwith.
Make the blade
Light as wind on water laid.
Make it long
As the wheat at harvest song.
Supple, swift
As a snake, without rift,
Full of lightnings, thousand-eyed!
Smooth as silken cloth and thin
As the web that spiders spin.
And merciless as pain, and cold."

"On the hilt what shall be told?"

"On the sword's hilt, my good man,"
Said the warrior of Japan,
"Trace for me
A running lake, a flock of sheep
And one who sings her child to sleep."

from the Yiddish
Yehoash (Solomon Bloomgarden)
Marie Syrkin

If thou art sleeping, maiden,
    Awake and open thy door.
'Tis the break of day, and we must away
    O'er meadow, and mount, and moor.

Wait not to find thy slippers,
    But come with thy naked feet;
We shall have to pass through the dewy grass
    And waters wide and fleet.

from the Spanish
Gil Vicente
Henry Wadsworth Longfellow

Airs! that wander and murmur round,
  Bearing delight where'er ye blow,—
Make in the elms a lulling sound,
  While my lady sleeps in the shade below.
Lighten and lengthen her noonday rest,
  Till the heat of the noonday sun is o'er:
Sweet be her slumbers,—though in my breast
  The pain she has waked may slumber no more!
Breathing soft from the blue profound,
  Bearing delight where'er ye blow,
Make in the elms a lulling sound,
  While my lady sleeps in the shade below.

Airs! that over the bending boughs,
  And under the shadows of the leaves,
Murmur soft, like my timid vows,
  Or the secret sighs my bosom heaves,—
Gently sweeping the grassy ground,
  Bearing delight where'er ye blow,
Make in the elms a lulling sound,
  While my lady sleeps in the shade below.

from the Spanish
Anonymous
William Cullen Bryant

Winter days and spring and summer still the yearly round re-
new;
And the Sun himself goes under, giving lady Night her due.
Weary not your soul with asking whence the sunshine, whence
the showers,
But where sweetest myrrh is selling, where the lover's crown of
flowers.
Piper, play on.

O for living streams of honey from a triple fountain spilling!
Five of milk, of wine ten other, and a dozen myrrh-distilling!
Add me two of fresh spring-water, three of snowy coldness add,
With a lad to every fountain and a lass to every lad.
Piper, play on.

Lydian pipe and lyre of Lydia work to make my holiday,
Phrygia's reed is never idle, timbrels tap their hides away.
Dear to me in life their music, and when death comes, I entreat,
Set the pipes above for headstone and a lyre to mark my feet.
Piper, play on.

from the Greek
Anonymous
T. F. Higham

the bliss
of
solitude

I and Pangur Bán, my cat,
'Tis a like task we are at;
Hunting mice is his delight,
Hunting words I sit all night.

Better far than praise of men
'Tis to sit with book and pen;
Pangur bears me no ill will,
He too plies his simple skill.

'Tis a merry thing to see
At our tasks how glad are we,
When at home we sit and find
Entertainment to our mind.

Oftentimes a mouse will stray
In the hero Pangur's way;
Oftentimes my keen thought set
Takes a meaning in its net.

'Gainst the wall he sets his eye
Full and fierce and sharp and sly;
'Gainst the wall of knowledge I
All my little wisdom try.

When a mouse darts from its den,
O how glad is Pangur then!
O what gladness do I prove
When I solve the doubts I love!

So in peace our tasks we ply,
Pangur Bán, my cat and I;
In our hearts we find our bliss,
I have mine and he has his.

Practice every day has made
Pangur perfect in his trade;
I get wisdom day and night
Turning darkness into light.

from the Irish
Anonymous
Robin Flower

At Matsushima

Islands all around,
each with its pine trees; and the wind—
how cool its sound!

from the Japanese
Shiki
Harold G. Henderson

The plants stand silent round me,
And the trees with light green leaves
Where slanting sunlight scatters
Its dust in yellow sheaves.

Far bells ring faintly over
The basking summerlands,
Vast and green and breathless
Round me the forest stands.

Only a lonely throstle
Trilling in yonder tree.
In the air a smell of forests,
In my heart, ecstasy.

from the Danish
Johannes Jorgensen
Robert Hillyer

I want to write a book of chaste and simple verse,
Sleep in an attic, like the old astrologers,
Up near the sky, and hear upon the morning air
The tolling of the bells. I want to sit and stare,
My chin in my two hands, out on the humming shops,
The weathervanes, the chimneys, and the steepletops
That rise like masts above the city, straight and tall,
And the mysterious big heavens over all.

How good, to watch the blue mist of the night come on,
The windows and the stars illumined, one by one,
The rivers of dark smoke pour upward lazily,
And the moon rise and turn them silver. I shall see
The springs, the summers, and the autumns slowly pass;
And when old Winter puts his blank face to the glass,
I shall close all my shutters, pull the curtains tight,
To build my palaces of sorcery in the night.

Then I shall dream of the horizons beyond wide
Gardens that mount into blue air,
Fountains that weep in alabaster, birds that sing
At dusk, at dawn—of every childish, idyllic thing.

The Insurrection, squalling vainly from below,
Will never cause my head to lift, I shall be so
Lost in that quiet ecstasy, the keenest still,
Of calling back the springtime at my own free will,
Of feeling a sun rise within me, fierce and hot,
And make a whole bright landscape of my burning thought.

from the French
Charles Baudelaire
George Dillon

I Built My Hut

I built my hut in a zone of human habitation,
Yet near me there sounds no noise of horse or coach.
   Would you know how that is possible?
A heart that is distant creates a wilderness round it.
I pluck chrysanthemums under the eastern hedge,
Then gaze long at the distant summer hills.
The mountain air is fresh at the dusk of day:
The flying birds two by two return.
In these things there lies a deep meaning;
Yet when we would express it, words suddenly fail us.

from the Chinese
T'ao Ch'ien
Arthur Waley

A hiding tuft, a green-barked yew-tree
  Is my roof,
While nearby a great oak keeps me
  Tempest-proof.

I can pick my fruit from an apple
  Like an inn,
Or can fill my fist where hazels
  Shut me in.

A clear well beside me offers
  Best of drink,
And there grows a bed of cresses
  Near its brink.

Pigs and goats, the friendliest neighbours,
  Nestle near,
Wild swine come, or broods of badgers,
  Grazing deer.

All the gentry of the county
  Come to call!
And the foxes come behind them,
  Best of all.

To what meals the woods invite me
   All about!
There are water, herbs and cresses,
   Salmon, trout.

A clutch of eggs, sweet mast and honey
   Are my meat,
Heathberries and whortleberries
   For a sweet.

All that one could ask for comfort
   Round me grows,
There are hips and haws and strawberries,
   Nuts and sloes.

And when summer spreads its mantle
   What a sight!
Marjoram and leeks and pignuts,
   Juicy, bright.

Dainty redbreasts briskly forage
   Every bush,
Round and round my hut there flutter
   Swallow, thrush.

Bees and beetles, music-makers,
  Croon and strum;
Geese pass over, duck in autumn,
  Dark streams hum.

Angry wren, officious linnet
  And black-cap,
All industrious, and the woodpeckers'
  Sturdy tap.

From the sea the gulls and herons
  Flutter in,
While in upland heather rises
  The grey hen.

In the year's most brilliant weather
  Heifers low
Through green fields, not driven nor beaten,
  Tranquil, slow.

In wreathed boughs the wind is whispering,
  Skies are blue,
Swans call, river water falling
  Is calling too.

from the Irish
Anonymous
Frank O'Connor

Peace

Courage, my Soul! now to the silent wood
Alone we wander, there to seek our food
In the wild fruits, and woo our dreamless sleep
  On soft boughs gathered deep.

There loud authority in folly bold,
And tongues that stammer with disease of gold,
And murmur of the windy world shall cease,
  Nor echo through our peace.

> from the Sanskrit
> *Bhartrihari*
> Paul Elmer More

Solitary Pine

  O solitary pine, how many
  Generations of man have you known?
  Is it because of your great age
  That the passing winds sing in so clear a tone?

> from the Japanese
> *Prince Ichihara*
> Ishii and Obata

Below the hall
The pine-trees grow in front of the steps,
Irregularly scattered,—not in ordered lines.
    Some are tall and some are low:
The tallest of them is six roods high;
    The lowest but ten feet.
    They are like wild things
    And no one knows who planted them.
They touch the walls of my blue-tiled house;
Their roots are sunk in the terrace of white sand.
Morning and evening they are visited by the wind and moon;
Rain or fine,—they are free from dust and mud.
In the gales of autumn they whisper a vague tune;
From the suns of summer they yield a cool shade.
At the height of spring the fine evening rain
Fills their leaves with a load of hanging pearls.
At the year's end the time of great snow
Stamps their branches with a fret of glittering jade.
Of the Four Seasons each has its own mood;
Among all the trees none is like another.
Last year, when they heard I had bought this house,
Neighbours mocked and the World called me mad—
That a whole family of twice ten souls
Should move house for the sake of a few pines!
Now that I have come to them, what have they given me?
They have only loosened the buckles of my care.

Yet even so, they are "profitable friends,"
And fill my need of "converse with wise men."
Yet when I consider how, still a man of the world,
In belt and cap I scurry through dirt and dust,
From time to time my heart twinges with shame
That I am not fit to be master of my pines!

from the Chinese
Po Chü-i
Arthur Waley

At Peace

Flowers every night
Blossom in the sky;
Peace in the Infinite;
At peace am I.

from the Persian
Rumi
A. J. Arberry

Fain would I live in safest freedom,
Free from the world, safe from its crowds.
Fain would I walk by quiet rivers,
Roofed by a shady tent of clouds.

Flurrying wings and summer feathers
Would brush my sullen days away.
Guilt-ridden men would shun the cleanness
Of air, the embrace of purity.

A boat upon a stream, forever,
Grazing the bank but rarely, drawn
To reach a young rose, and returning
To the mid-current running on.

Watching the herds far off, at pasture,
Fresh-hearted flowers every spring,
Vinemen lopping the grape harvest,
Reapers at the heady haymaking.

For food I'd have the light of heaven,
Bright, unstained, it cannot change!
And I would drink the living wellspring,
That blood might rest, not race and range.

from the German
August, Graf von Platen
Edwin Morgan

Here in the mountains the moon I love,
Hanging alight in a distant grove;
Pitying me in my loneliness,
She reaches a finger and touches my dress.
  My heart resembles the moon;
  The moon resembles my heart.
My heart and the moon in each other delight,
Each watching the other throughout the long night.

from the Chinese
Chen Shan-min
E. D. Edwards

Only a bell, a bird, the stillness break . . .
It seems the two are talking with the twilight.
The silence is of gold, the evening crystal.
A vagrant purity rocks the tender trees.
And, beyond it all, one dreams a limpid stream
That, trampling pearls, flees toward the infinite . . .
Solitude! Solitude! All is clear and calm . . .
Only a bell, a bird, the stillness break . . .
Love lives afar . . . serene, indifferent,
The heart is free. It is neither sad nor glad.
Colors, breezes, songs, perfumes distract it . . .
It swims as on a lake immune to sentiment . . .
Only a bell, a bird, the stillness break . . .
One seems to catch the eternal in one's hand!

from the Spanish
Juan Ramón Jiménez
Edward F. Gahan

Planting Flowers on the Eastern Embankment

I took money and bought flowering trees
And planted them out on the bank to the east of the Keep.
I simply bought whatever had most blooms,
Not caring whether peach, apricot, or plum.

A hundred fruits, all mixed up together;
A thousand branches, flowering in due rotation.
Each has its season coming early or late;
But to all alike the fertile soil is kind.
The red flowers gleam like a heavy mist;
The white flowers gleam like a fall of snow.
The wandering bees cannot bear to leave them;
The sweet birds also come there to roost.
In front there flows an ever-running stream;
Beneath there is built a little flat terrace.
Sometimes I sweep the flagstones of the terrace;
Sometimes, in the wind, I raise my cup and drink.
The flower-branches screen my head from the sun;
The flower-buds fall down into my lap.
Alone drinking, alone singing my songs
I do not notice that the moon is level with the steps.
The people of Pa do not care for flowers;
All the spring no one has come to look.
But their Governor General, alone with his cup of wine
Sits till evening and will not move from the place!

from the Chinese
Po Chü-i
Arthur Waley

When o'er the waters' azure trail
The zephyr glides with soft addresses
And fans the ships in pride of sail
And skiffs upon the wave caresses,
Then trouble's throbbing load I shed,
More joy in idle ease revealing:
My muse is still; her songs are fled;
The sea's soft tones are more appealing.
But when the billows crash the shore
And seething foam in tumult splashes
And thunder-claps from heaven roar
And lightning through the darkness flashes,
Then I from sea-washed shores remove
And hospitable woods receive me;
Dry earth, more safe, deserves my love;
The fisherman's stern labours grieve me.
The skiff wherein he plies is frail,
The sport of eddies blind with riot;
But river-music from the vale
I hear, secure in haunts of quiet.

from the Russian
Alexander Pushkin
Sir Cecil Kisch

Trees growing—right in front of my window;
The trees are high and the leaves grow thick.
Sad alas! the distant mountain view
Obscured by this, dimly shows between.
One morning I took knife and axe;
With my own hand I lopped the branches off.
Ten thousand leaves fall about my head;
A thousand hills come before my eyes.
Suddenly, as when clouds or mists break
And straight through, the blue sky appears;
Again, like the face of a friend one has loved
Seen at last after an age of parting.
First there came a gentle wind blowing;
One by one the birds flew back to the tree.
To ease my mind I gazed to the South East;
As my eyes wandered, my thoughts went far away.
Of men there is none that has not some preference;
Of things there is none but mixes good with ill.
It was not that I did not love the tender branches;
But better still,—to see the green hills!

from the Chinese
Po Chü-i
Arthur Waley

This lonely hill has always
Been dear to me, and this thicket
Which shuts out most of the final
Horizon from view. I sit here,
And gaze, and imagine
The interminable spaces
That stretch away, beyond my mind,
Their uncanny silences,
Their profound calms; and my heart
Is almost overwhelmed with dread.
And when the wind drones in the
Branches, I compare its sound
With that infinite silence;
And I think of eternity,
And the dead past, and the living
Present, and the sound of it;
And my thought drowns in immensity;
And shipwreck is sweet in such a sea.

from the Italian
Giacomo Leopardi
Kenneth Rexroth

In the month of June the grass grows high
And round my cottage thick-leaved branches sway.
There is not a bird but delights in the place where it rests:
And I too—love my thatched cottage.
I have done my ploughing:
I have sown my seed.
Again I have time to sit and read my books.
In the narrow lane there are no deep ruts:
Often my friends' carriages turn back.
In high spirits I pour out my spring wine
And pluck the lettuce growing in my garden.
A gentle rain comes stealing up from the east
And a sweet wind bears it company.
My thoughts float idly over the story of King Chou,
My eyes wander over the pictures of Hills and Seas.
At a single glance I survey the whole Universe.
He will never be happy, whom such pleasures fail to please!

from the Chinese
T'ao Ch'ien
Arthur Waley

Lonely I lay in the heather-soft hollow,
Rudely the storm wind came thundering by,
Moss-covered gravestones I had for my pillow,
Letting my gaze roam far up in the sky.

Then as I gazed I would hum little tunes there,
Lost in my thoughts, as the clouds raced along.
Storms were forgotten—the naked-backed dunes there
Heard the first strains of my desolate song.

Oft through the storm would be heard intimations
Born of some gentler and happier time;
And to my spirit the tender vibrations
Softly o'er ocean and heathland would chime.

Oft even there would the sun shine to bless me,
Moonlight and stars in the heavens would bloom;
Tempest and fog would not always oppress me,
Shrouding my heather with grayness and gloom.

Gloomy and gray is my land's native heather,
Thick, though, beneath it the wee flowers throng;
And o'er the graves in the mild April weather
Larks thrill the waste with a rapture of song.

from the Danish
Steen Steensen Blicher
Charles Wharton Stork

Happy the man, and happy he alone,
He, who can call today his own:
He who secure within, can say,
Tomorrow do thy worst, for I have lived today.
Be fair or foul, or rain or shine,
The joys I have possessed, in spite of fate, are mine.
Not Heaven itself upon the past has power,
But what has been, has been, and I have had my hour.

from the Latin
Horace
John Dryden

When winds that move not its calm surface sweep
The azure sea, I love the land no more;
The smiles of the serene and tranquil deep
Tempt my unquiet mind. —But when the roar
Of Ocean's gray abyss resounds, and foam
Gathers upon the sea, and vast waves burst,
I turn from the drear aspect to the home
Of Earth and its deep woods, where, interspersed,
When winds blow loud, pines make sweet melody.
Whose house is some lone bark, whose toil the sea,
Whose prey the wandering fish, an evil lot
Has chosen. —But I my languid limbs will fling
Beneath the plane, where the brook's murmuring
Moves the calm spirit, but disturbs it not.

from the Greek
Moschus
Percy Bysshe Shelley

Could I take me to some cavern for mine hiding,
  In the hilltops where the Sun scarce hath trod;
Or a cloud make the home of mine abiding,
  As a bird among the bird-droves of God.
Could I wing me to my rest amid the roar
Of the deep Adriatic on the shore
Where the water of Eridanus is clear,
  And Phaeton's sad sisters by his grave
Weep into the river, and each tear
  Gleams a drop of amber, in the wave.

To the strand of the Daughters of the Sunset,
  The Apple-tree, the singing and the gold;
Where the mariner must stay him from his onset,
  And the red wave is tranquil as of old;
    Yea, beyond that pillar of the End
    That Atlas guardeth, would I wend;
Where a voice of living waters never ceaseth
  In God's quiet garden by the sea,
And Earth, the ancient life-giver, increaseth
  Joy among the meadows, like a tree.

from the Greek
Euripides
Gilbert Murray

Live so that you tempt not the sea relentless,
Neither press too close on the shore forbidding;
Flee extremes, and choose thou the mean all-golden,
    Treasure all priceless.

Safe, you dread not poverty's hut repellent;
Wise, you seek not mansions that men may envy;
All secure, protected by moderation,
    Fate cannot harm you.

Tallest pines are soon by the storm blasts shattered,
Turrets high may fall with the loudest clamor,
Tow'ring peaks are seared by the lightning's fury,
    Dangerous, earth's summits.

Lighten grief with hopes of a brighter morrow;
Temper joy, in fear of a change of fortune;
Bear the winters, knowing, despite their fury,
    Jove will recall them.

If, today, misfortune besiege thy pathway,
Still the future beckons a smiling promise;
Soon Apollo leaving his arrows dreaded
    Makes the Muse tuneful.

Thus in stormy days be of heart courageous
And, when waves are calm, and the danger over,
Wise man, trim your sails when a gale too prosp'rous
    Swells out the canvas.

from the Latin
Horace
Margaret M. Fitzgerald

Be Still, My Soul

Heart, my heart, with griefs confounded whence you no
    deliv'rance find,
Up against them! guard yourself and show the foe a gallant
    breast;
Take your stand among the foremost where the spears of battle
    fly
Gallantly. Nor when you conquer make your pleasure manifest,
Nor in turn, if you are conquered, lie down in your home and
    cry.
Take your joy when life is joyful, and in sorrow do not mind
Overmuch, but know what ups and downs belong to human-
    kind.

from the Greek
Archilochus
C. M. Bowra

O Gentle Sleep, that teachest man to die
With a calm foretaste of eternity,
Lull for a little space this mortal frame
And let the soul go roving like a flame.
Where the bright day is walking on the sea,
Or where the evening shadows hide the lea,
Or where the ice and snowfield reign supreme,
Or where hot summers dry the desert stream;
Free, at the stars of heaven, let it gaze
In nearer, bolder aspect as they blaze;
Enraptured let it hearken to the sound
Of wheeling planets on their ceaseless round!
So may the poor thing rove with burning zest,
While the dull body, that desires rest,
Untouch'd by any yearning feels the peace
That it shall enter when its annals cease!

from the Polish
Jan Kochanowski
Watson Kirkconnell

Dark house, dark lonely grave,
Within your walls,
Under yew-boughs, there is quiet sleep;
And not a trace of care,
But deep forgetting on man's being falls.
There nothing, not a creature calls
Unless those fragile airs
That stir the little leaves
Say something to the secret mound
Of many burials.
Dark house, your hours have never known
The hurry and the passion of our days.
Within that heart of stone
Love never beat, nor hate could live.
Nothing at all is left,
Unless in that damp cell
The dead may have a dream he cannot tell.

from the Welsh
T. Gwynn Jones
Ernest Rhys

Cliffs that rise a thousand feet
Without a break,
Lake that stretches a hundred miles
Without a wave,
Sands that are white through all the year,
Without a stain,
Pine-tree woods, winter and summer
Ever-green,
Streams that for ever flow and flow
Without a pause,
Trees that for twenty thousand years
Your vows have kept,
You have suddenly healed the pain of a traveller's heart,
And moved his brush to write a new song.

from the Chinese
Chan Fang-shēng
Arthur Waley

On the Mountain Pass

Here on the mountain pass,
somehow they draw one's heart so—
violets in the grass.

from the Japanese
Matsuo Bashō
Harold G. Henderson

An arrow flying past,
a shaft shot in the dark
without a thought of where
its trembling point will strike;

A dry leaf from the tree
tossed by the autumn gales,
and no one knows what furrow
will catch it when it falls;

A giant wave that the wind
whips and drives through the sea,
that rolls on without knowing
which is the shore it seeks;

Lamp that, as it expires,
casts trembling rings of light
and knows not which will prove
its final shining out.

All these am I who wander
across the world, nor see
whence I have come or whither
my steps will carry me.

from the Spanish
Gustavo Adolfo Bécquer
J. M. Cohen

What man is he that yearneth
For length unmeasured of days?
Folly mine eye discerneth
Encompassing all his ways.
For years over-running the measure
Shall change thee in evil wise:
Grief draweth nigh thee; and pleasure,
Behold, it is hid from thine eyes.
This to their wage have they
Which overlive their day.
And He that looseth from labour
Doth one with other befriend,
Whom bride nor bridesmen attend,
Song, nor sound of the tabor,
Death, that maketh an end.
Thy portion esteem I highest,
Who wast not ever begot;
Thine next, being born who diest
And straightway again art not.
With follies light as the feather
Doth Youth to man befall;
Then evils gather together,
There wants not one of them all—
Wrath, envy, discord, strife,
The sword that seeketh life.

And sealing the sum of trouble
  Doth tottering Age draw nigh,
  Whom friends and kinsfolk fly,
Age, upon whom redouble
  All sorrows under the sky.

This man, as me, even so,
Have the evil days overtaken;
And like as a cape sea-shaken
With tempest at earth's last verges
And shock of all winds that blow,
His head the seas of woe,
The thunders of awful surges
Ruining overflow;
Blown from the fall of even,
  Blown from the dayspring forth,
Blown from the noon in heaven,   ˙
  Blown from night and the North.

from the Greek
Sophocles
A. E. Housman

Tears flow in my heart
As rain falls on the town;
What languor is this
That creeps into my heart?

Gentle sound of the rain
On earth and roofs!
For an aching heart
Is the song of the rain!

Tears flow senseless
In this breaking heart.
With no betrayal?
This grief is senseless.

This is the worst sorrow
Not to know why,
Without love or hate,
My heart has all this sorrow.

from the French
Paul Verlaine
Muriel Kittel

No sky at all;
   no earth at all—and still
      the snowflakes fall. . . .

from the Japanese
Hashin
Harold G. Henderson

Far Beyond Us

As the moon sinks on the mountain-edge
The fishermen's lights flicker
Far out on the dark wide sea.

When we think that we alone
Are steering our ships at midnight,
We hear the splash of oars
Far beyond us.

from the Japanese
Anonymous
Ishii and Obata

Will they ever come to me, ever again,
　　The long long dances,
On through the dark till the dawn-stars wane?
Shall I feel the dew on my throat, and the stream
Of wind in my hair? Shall our white feet gleam
　　In the dim expanses?
Oh, feet of a fawn to the greenwood fled,
　　Alone in the grass and the loveliness;
Leap of the hunted, no more in dread,
　　Beyond the snares and the deadly press:
Yet a voice still in the distance sounds,
A voice and a fear and a haste of hounds;
O wildly labouring, fiercely fleet,
　　Onward yet by river and glen . . .
Is it joy or terror, ye storm-swift feet? . . .
　　To the dear lone lands untroubled of men,
Where no voice sounds, and amid the shadowy green
The little things of the woodland live unseen.

What else is Wisdom? What of man's endeavour
　　Or God's high grace, so lovely and so great?
　　To stand from fear set free, to breathe and wait;
　　To hold a hand uplifted over Hate;
And shall not Loveliness be loved for ever?

Happy he, on the weary sea
Who hath fled the tempest and won the haven.
Happy whoso hath risen free,
Above his striving. For strangely graven
Is the orb of life, that one and another
In gold and power may outpass his brother.
And men in their millions float and flow
And seethe with a million hopes as leaven;
And they win their Will, or they miss their Will,
And their hopes are dead or are pined for still;
But whoe'er can know,
As the long days go,
That to Live is happy, hath found his Heaven.

from the Greek
Euripides
Gilbert Murray

So still the pond in morning's gray,
A quiet conscience is not clearer.
When west winds kiss its glassy mirror,
The sedges do not feel it sway.
Above it throbs the dragonfly;
Blue-gold and crimson cross and ply.
And where the sun reflected glances,
The water spider skips and dances.
On the bank a lilied ring scarce blows;
The reedy lullaby will not cease.
A rippling rustle comes and goes,
As though it whispered: peace, peace, peace.

from the German
Annette von Droste-Hülshoff
Herman Salinger

all

glorious

above

Let nothing disturb thee,
Nothing affright thee;
All things are passing;
God never changeth;
Patient endurance
Attaineth to all things;
Who God possesseth
In nothing is wanting;
Alone God sufficeth.

from the Spanish
St. Teresa of Avila
Henry Wadsworth Longfellow

We are the flute, our music is all Thine;
We are the mountains echoing only Thee;
Pieces of chess Thou marshallest in line
And movest to defeat or victory;
Lions emblazoned high on flags unfurled—
Thy wind invisible sweeps us through the world.

from the Persian
Rumi
R. A. Nicholson

Conversation in the Mountains

If you were to ask me why I dwell among green mountains,
I should laugh silently; my soul is serene.
The peach blossom follows the moving water;
There is another heaven and earth beyond the world of men.

from the Chinese
Li Po
Anonymous

O Lord our Lord,
How excellent is thy name in all the earth!
Who hast set thy glory above the heavens.
Out of the mouth of babes and sucklings hast thou ordained
    strength
Because of thine enemies,
That thou mightest still the enemy and the avenger.
When I consider thy heavens, the work of thy fingers,
The moon and the stars, which thou hast ordained;
What is man, that thou art mindful of him?
And the son of man, that thou visitest him?
For thou hast made him a little lower than the angels,
And hast crowned him with glory and honour.
Thou madest him to have dominion over the works of thy
    hands;
Thou has put all things under his feet:
All sheep and oxen,
Yea, and the beasts of the field;
The fowl of the air, and the fish of the sea,
And whatsoever passeth through the paths of the seas.
O Lord our Lord,
How excellent is thy name in all the earth!

from the Hebrew
The Old Testament
King James Version

Wonders are many, but there is no wonder
　Wilder than Man—
Man who makes the winds of winter bear him,
Through the trough of waves that tower about him,
Across grey wastes of sea;
Man who wearies the Untiring, the Immortal—
Earth, eldest of the Gods, as year by year,
His plough-teams come and go.
The care-free bands of birds,
Beasts of the wild, tribes of the sea,
In netted toils he takes,
The Subtle One.
Creatures that haunt the hills, the desert-dwellers,
His cunning snares; he lays his mastering yoke
On the horse's shaggy mane,
On the tireless mountain-bull.
Speech, too, and wind-swift thought
And the soul of the ruler of cities
He hath learned, untaught of any.
To shun the bitter arrows of the roofless frost,
The bitter shafts of rain,
He knows, the all-deviser; for without device
No morrow finds him. Only against Death
He shall call for help in vain,
Yet many a mortal sickness he hath mastered.

Thus with his wisdom,
Subtle past foretelling,
Man wins to joy, or sorrow.
Does he keep his native laws
And the justice sworn by heaven?—
High stands his city. But all citiless
Wanders the wretch that dares make sin his fellow.
May never such transgressor
Share hearth, nor heart, of mine!

from the Greek
Sophocles
F. L. Lucas

Perfection ever rising to perfection,
The man who fashioned mountains and rocks!
Purity Immaculate,
Wood white and unblemished.

Guardian of nation upon nation,
Lone creator of firmament and horizon!
Origin of nation upon nation!
Even before birth the King!

The one of there! The one of here!
The one of here! The one of there!
The one of everywhere, above and below!
The knower of all!
The beautiful knower of the innermost!
Lord of wisdom, above and below!
The depth too deep for the measure stick.

Lord of heaven's vault!
Lord of that which endeth not! Lord of the everlasting!
The rock which has withstood the fire!
Lord of that which endeth not, both the going out and the
    coming back.
That which endeth not is never understood.
King of kings, an unfathomable thought!

I, the mother, even though scandal is spoken,
Yet ever and again we clap hands,
And all slides off my shoulders.
The rock has been fashioned a shining beacon on the mountain
    top.
Thither we flee from raging storms.
Knife carving portions for others,
Yet, the while, carving for the master himself.
Where the front hoof has trod,
There also shall the back hoof tread.

from the Sotho (African)
Anonymous
G. H. Franz

The prayers I make will then be sweet indeed,
If Thou the spirit give by which I pray:
My unassisted heart is barren clay,
Which of its native self can nothing feed:
Of good and pious works Thou art the seed,
Which quickens only where Thou say'st it may;
Unless Thou show to us Thine own true way,
No man can find it: Father! Thou must lead.
Do Thou, then, breathe those thoughts into my mind
By which such virtue may in me be bred
That in Thy holy footsteps I may tread;
The fetters of my tongue do Thou unbind,
That I may have the power to sing of Thee,
And sound Thy praises everlastingly.

from the Italian
Michelangelo Buonarroti
William Wordsworth

Psalm Twenty-Four

The earth is the Lord's, and the fulness thereof;
The world, and they that dwell therein.
For he hath founded it upon the seas,
And established it upon the floods.

Who shall ascend into the hill of the Lord?
Or who shall stand in his holy place?
He that hath clean hands, and a pure heart;
Who hath not lifted up his soul unto vanity, nor sworn deceit-
    fully.
He shall receive the blessing from the Lord,
And righteousness from the God of his salvation.
This is the generation of them that seek him,
That seek thy face, O Jacob.
Lift up your heads, O ye gates;
And be ye lift up, ye everlasting doors;
And the King of glory shall come in.
Who is this King of glory?
The Lord strong and mighty,
The Lord mighty in battle.
Lift up your heads, O ye gates;
Even lift them up, ye everlasting doors;
And the King of glory shall come in.
Who is this King of glory?
The Lord of hosts,
He is the King of glory.

from the Hebrew
The Old Testament
King James Version

Prayer

Merciful God, who readst my inmost mind,
I flee to Thee, and would, but cannot pray.
Behold my downcast spirit, my eyes purblind
With streaming tears no soothing words can stay.

I do not ask for aught, a broken reed.
My baffled senses grip me in their hold.
Thou alone knowest what Thy child does need.
Thy love exceeds his self-love, thousandfold.

To Thine unknowing son make up his loss.
He dares not ask for aught, nor even knows.
I bow me down, beg neither cure nor cross.
Do as Thy infinite mercy may dispose.

Yea, wound or heal, raise up or down my mind.
I shall adore Thy will, dark though it be.
I offer up myself, still and resigned.
All that I ask for is to rest in Thee.

I look to Thee in awe, as children may,
With Christian hope no petulance impair.
O teach me, God, what Thou wilt let me pray.
Pray Thou Thyself in me and cleanse my prayer.

from the Dutch
Willem Bilderdijk
A. J. Barnouw

Psalm One Hundred Fifty

Praise ye the Lord.
Praise God in his sanctuary:
Praise him in the firmament of his power.
Praise him for his mighty acts:
Praise him according to his excellent greatness.
Praise him with the sound of the trumpet:
Praise him with the psaltery and harp.
Praise him with the timbrel and dance:
Praise him with stringed instruments and organs.
Praise him upon the loud cymbals:
Praise him upon the high-sounding cymbals.
Let every thing that hath breath praise the Lord.
Praise ye the Lord.

from the Hebrew
The Old Testament
King James Version

As salt resolved in the ocean
I was swallowed in God's sea,
Past faith, past unbelieving,
Past doubt, past certainty.

Suddenly in my bosom
A star shone clear and bright;
All the suns of heaven
Vanished in that star's light.

from the Persian
Rumi
A. J. Arberry

The Song of the Creatures

O most high, almighty, good Lord God,
To Thee belong praise, glory, honor and all blessing!

Praised be my Lord God with all His creatures,
And especially our brother the sun,
Who brings us the day and who brings us the light;
Fair is he and shines with very great splendor;
O Lord, he signifies to us Thee!

Praised be my Lord for our sister the moon,
And for the stars, the which He has set clear and lovely in
    heaven.

Praised be my Lord for our brother the wind,
And for air and cloud calms and all weather
By which Thou upholdest life in all creatures—

Praised be my Lord for all those who pardon one another,
For His love's sake,
And who endure weakness and tribulation;
Blessèd are they who peaceably shall endure.
For Thou, O Most Highest, shalt give them a crown!

Praised be my Lord for our sister, the death of the body,
From which no man escapeth.
Woe to him who dieth in mortal sin!
Blessèd are they who are found walking by Thy most holy will,
For the second death shall have no power to do them harm.

Praise ye and bless the Lord,
And give thanks unto Him and serve Him with great humility.

from the Italian
St. Francis of Assisi
Matthew Arnold

When waves invade the yellowing wheat,
And the saplings sway with a wind-song brief;
When the raspberry plum in the garden sweet
Hides him under the cool green leaf;

When sprinkled with lights of limpid dew,
At rose of evening or gold of morn,
The lilies-of-the-valley strew
Their silver nodding under the thorn;

When the brook in the valley with cooling breast,
Plunging my soul in a cloudy dream,
Murmurs a legend of lands of rest
At the rise of his happy and rapid stream;

Then humbled is my heart's distress,
And lulled the anguish of my blood;
Then in the earth my happiness,
Then in the heaven my God.

from the Russian
Mikhail Yuryevich Lermontov
Max Eastman

Who knows, when raindrops are descending,
　　Which thirsty seed will highest grow?
Who knows, when Sabbath knees are bending,
　　Where God will greatest grace bestow?

Since it shall rain alike on all—
　　On ploughland as on stony ground—
Shall any tear unnoticed fall?
　　Shall any lost sheep not be found?

Who knows what status God has given—
　　Who here on earth is small, who great?
Each grass-blade feels the growth of heaven,
　　Each raindrop shares the ocean's fate.

from the Icelandic
Einar Benediktsson
Watson Kirkconnell

The strong man awhile in his kingdom is lord,
Like eagles his glory is flying;
But broken at last is the conquering sword,
And the eagles in dust will be lying.
What Might has created is short-lived and vain:
Like winds of the desert it passes again.

But Truth lives forever. Though weapons be whirled,
Her brow shines undimmed o'er the pother.
'Tis she that leads on through the night of this world
And points us the way to another.
The True is eternal: from heaven to earth
With each generation the word echoes forth.

The Right is eternal: though trod in the dust,
Yet never her lily shall perish.
Though Evil have won all the world from the just,
Your will yet availeth to cherish.
Though Force and Deceit all without may have reft,
Yet hid in your bosom a stronghold is left.

The fiery will which was barred from its choice
Takes form, like to God, and is action.
The Right finds a weapon, the True finds a voice,
Men rise up in bold insurrection.
The gifts you have brought and the dangers you've run
Arise out of Lethe like stars, every one.

And Poetry's not as a bow in the sky,
Or volatile perfume of flowers.
The beauty you make is not dust that shall die,
The ages but quicken its powers.
Eternal is Beauty, its metal sublime
We ardently seek in the waters of Time.

Then seize on all Truth, venture all for the Right,
Make Beauty with joy for your wages!
These three from humanity never take flight,
With them we appeal to the ages.
Whatever Time gave, unto Time you must pay,
The Eternal alone dwells within you for aye.

from the Swedish
Esaias Tegnér
Charles Wharton Stork

I have sought Thee daily at dawn and twilight,
   I have stretched my hands to Thee, turned my face,
Now the cry of a heart athirst I will utter,
   Like the beggar who cries at my door for grace.
The infinite heights are too small to contain Thee,
   Yet perchance Thou canst niche in the clefts of me.
Shall my heart not treasure the hope to gain Thee,
   Or my yearning fail till my tongue's last plea?
   Nay, surely Thy name I will worship, while breath in my
     nostrils be.

from the Hebrew
Solomon Ibn-Gabirol
Israel Zangwill

Virtue dwells, so runs the tale,
On precipices hard to scale.
Swift holy Nymphs attend her place;
No mortal eyes may see her face,
But only he, who with distress
Of soul and sweating heart can press
On to the height in manliness.

from the Greek
Simonides
C. M. Bowra

An Eclipse

When God reveals his plans to men,
Straight is the way to glory then
And good the end for all;
And God can from the murky night
Create inviolable light
Or hide the stainless day from sight
Beneath a black cloud's pall.

from the Greek
Pindar
C. M. Bowra

The Dead Man Ariseth and Singeth a Hymn to the Sun.

Homage to thee, O Ra, at thy tremendous rising!
Thou risest! Thou shinest! the heavens are rolled aside!
Thou art the King of Gods, thou art the All-comprising,
From thee we come, in thee are deified.

Thy priests go forth at dawn; they wash their hearts with
    laughter;
Divine winds move in music across thy golden strings.
At sunset they embrace thee, as every cloudy rafter
Flames with reflected color from thy wings.

Thou sailest over the zenith, and thy heart rejoices;
Thy Morning Boat and Evening Boat with fair winds meet
    together;
Before thy face the goddess Maat exalts her fateful Feather,
And at thy name the halls of Anu ring with voices.

O Thou Perfect! Thou Eternal! Thou Only One!
Great Hawk that fliest with the flying Sun!
Between the Turquoise Sycamores that risest, young for ever,
Thine image flashing on the bright celestial river.

Thy rays are on all faces; Thou art inscrutable.
Age after age thy life renews its eager prime.
Time whirls its dust beneath thee; thou art immutable,
Maker of Time, thyself beyond all Time.

Thou passest through the portals that close behind the night,
Gladdening the souls of them that lay in sorrow.
The True of Word, the Quiet Heart, arise to drink thy light;
Thou art To-day and Yesterday; Thou art To-morrow!

Homage to thee, O Ra, who wakest life from slumber!
Thou risest! Thou shinest! Thy radiant face appears!
Millions of years have passed,—we can not count their num-
    ber,—
Millions of years shall come. Thou art above the years!

from the Egyptian
The Book of the Dead
Robert Hillyer

index of authors and sources

213

index of titles

index of first lines

index of translators

index of languages